Doctor By Nature

Jonathan Couch
Surgeon of Polperro

Jeremy Rowett Johns

ISBN HB 978-095595412-2
ISBN 978-095595413-9

A catalogue record for this book is available from the British Library.

Published in Great Britain in 2010 by
Polperro Heritage Press,
Clifton-upon-Teme, Worcestershire WR6 6EN UK
www.polperropress.co.uk

Cover design by
Steve Bowgen

Printed by
Orphans Press
Leominster, Herefordshire
United Kingdom

Acknowledgements

In the course of writing this book I have relied extensively on the unpublished work of two Polperro historians and authors who are no longer with us, James Derriman and Sheila de Burlet. In addition, I have received advice and assistance from a number of people, in particular Martin Hipperson for his transcription of Jonathan Couch's medical notebook; and Philip Correll, Sue Dent, Carole Vivian, Enid Wenban and the late Sir John Trelawny. I am also grateful for the help I have received from Angela Broome, Librarian at the Courtney Library of the Royal Institution of Cornwall; Lynda Brooks and Ben Sherwood at the Library of the Linnean Society of London; Alison Spence and Jennie Hancock at the Cornwall Records Office; Kim Cooper at the Cornwall Studies Library in Redruth; Ann and Mike Gill at Couch's House in Polperro; John and Glen Feesey at Lansallos; Valerie-Anne Lutz at the American Philosophical Society Library in Philadelphia, and Dr. Paddy Matthews for his advice on medical matters. And finally, special thanks are due to Fiona Thompson who so painstakingly edited the text and made a great many helpful suggestions for improving it; my son Barney for his helpful and constructive comments on the text, and Christine Hipperson for checking the final proof.

To Sue for her enduring patience and support throughout

Illustrations

Contents

INTRODUCTION

In the summer of 1850 an enormous sea monster entangled itself in the drift net of a boat fishing for mackerel off the Cornish coast. Alarmed by its desperate struggle to escape but unwilling to cut it free, the crew decided to tow it back to harbour where, on arrival, they sent word to inform the local doctor of the catch. Jonathan Couch quickly took leave of his medical practice, collected his sketch-book and made his way down to the quayside where the fishermen had obligingly lifted the huge carcase out of the water for him to examine. It was, he declared on close inspection, an unusual species of whale. Seating himself on an inverted fish basket, he set to work drawing the creature, taking particular care to capture the dark bluish black hue of its skin before the colours faded.

It was a familiar scene: the doctor, dressed in his customary long black coat, surrounded by a curious but admiring crowd of fishermen, boys and women with their knitting, preserving yet another image of marine life for posterity. For Jonathan Couch was a country doctor who chose to work quietly at home in a remote fishing village on the south coast of Cornwall, observing the birds of the air, the fish of the sea and the creatures that move on the earth and he came to be numbered among the great scientific figures of his day. He never courted fame but found it anyway. Rather, fame had to come looking for him down a steep and rocky road on a distant shore. He devoted his life to, and built his reputation upon, painstaking study of the natural world in that corner of England. At the same time he was also caring for the bodies and souls of his neighbours, the families of fishermen and farmers around Polperro where he was born and had his being.

Jonathan Couch was a quietly remarkable man in a remarkably noisy age: the tumultuous, heroic, inventive, often cruel and always rapidly-expanding, full-steam world of nineteenth century Britain with all its energy and thirst for discovery. Here, through time of war, political and religious turmoil and impassioned debate in science, he followed his own intellectual path. Great events might occur elsewhere but the good doctor could be found – as likely as not – sitting on the quay, sketching some newly-found specimen fresh from the sea. He made Cornwall his own Galapagos, a place of discovery.

He came into this vigorous world at a time when it was still possible for a gifted individual not only to grasp and follow advances across a range of disciplines but to achieve distinction in wholly separate fields. And he never ceased to learn. It was eventually said of this diligent man: 'his highest pleasure was to be a learner and a student.' At the very outset, as a young man, he turned his back on the opportunity of a lucrative medical career in London. Instead he chose to serve with devotion the people of his native village as their surgeon-apothecary and man-midwife for 60 years. He certainly didn't turn away from medical innovation. He was, for instance, not afraid to fight smallpox through the then still novel means of inoculation and vaccination – and not shy of blaming the spread of disease on poor housing and squalid standards of public hygiene. Late in his long life, he was proud to have known six generations of local families and to have attended four generations in childbirth. 'If Dr Couch gave a patient up it was no use to call anyone else in. You might just as well curl up your toes and die,' said his local patients.

But that is only a fraction of the story. Jonathan Couch was possessed of an extraordinarily inquiring mind. In the severe winter of 1795, the five-year-old Jonathan witnessed a salmon frozen so rigid it could be made to stand upright on its tail. It is not difficult to trace a life-long, all-embracing passion for natural science to that small boy's fascination with a spectacle he would remember all his days. He was a pioneering natural scientist; a world-leading, astonishingly diligent observer of animal behaviour; a trail-blazer for Charles Darwin and other scientific thinkers of towering stature. The doctor was the authority on the fish species native to British waters, recording their physiology in loving detail. But his lively mind also turned to the migration of birds and the habits of bats; he wrote about fossils and flowering plants, sharks and shooting stars, porpoises and potato disease, crabs and carpenter bees. He was an early advocate of conservation who worried about overfishing; a recorder of species of fish and birds previously unknown to science, often brought to his door by seagoing neighbours or else picked up on the wayside during his medical rounds.

His reputation is secured by his great works, notably his four-volume *History of the Fishes of the British Islands*, a gargantuan effort which became and remains a standard source of reference, quoted by Darwin among others. His name is enshrined in small things: a species of woodlouse bears his name, *Philoscia couchii*, a previously unrecorded type of coral is called, in his honour, *Rhodophyton couchii*. Couch's Whiting swims off Cornwall's rugged coast; the Dotted Mackerel owes its discrete identity to the man-midwife of Polperro.

Of all the distinctions that came his way he was, perhaps, most proud of his election as a Fellow of the Linnean Society, which placed him among the ranks of the most distinguished men of science of the day. And what a day: the golden age of discovery and classification of species, a field pioneered by the Swedish naturalist Carl Linnaeus. The learned society was formed 'for the cultivation of the science of natural history' – and Jonathan Couch was from the moment of his nomination pleased to use the letters FLS after his name.

He was a classical scholar; a Methodist preacher; an antiquarian and gatherer of Cornish words; a force behind road and bridge-building works; a tireless correspondent generating innumerable letters, learned papers and published works. And he was also a compassionate family man, himself acquainted with grief. His three marriages yielded 11 children and more than a fair share of loss – his first wife died, devastatingly, only nine weeks after their wedding day. Happily, there is another measure of fame to be found among Jonathan's progeny: Sir Arthur Quiller-Couch, man of letters and collector of English verse (still remembered by the pen name: Q), was his grandson.

On his death Jonathan Couch was honoured with this epitaph: 'His memory is precious and endures'. The purpose of this book is to show that it is - and it does.

CHAPTER I

A LIVELY AND ENQUIRING MIND

Four months before the storming of the Bastille in Paris that sparked the French Revolution in 1789, a 44-year-old fish-curer's wife gave birth to a baby boy on Sunday, March 15, in a room by the harbour in Polperro, a remote fishing village on the south coast of Cornwall. He was the sole offspring of Richard and Philippa Couch, a god-fearing Methodist couple who lived in what is now Warren Cottage at the bottom of the Calvinist's Steps. Four weeks later, the child was carried up over the hill to Talland church by his parents where he was baptised and named Jonathan.

So it was that one of the more remarkable figures in Cornish history entered the world. In Polperro at the end of the eighteenth century most families were engaged in either fishing or farming. The fishing industry served to keep most men busy and reasonably prosperous. Whole families could live for months on the proceeds of one good haul of fish. Among them were the Couches, one of whom fought at the Battle of Trafalgar; another died in the frozen wastes of the Arctic along with the rest of Sir John Franklin's ill-fated 1845 expedition to find the Northwest Passage. Of that original family of yeoman farmers, Richard alone remained in Polperro; a prosperous fish merchant profiting from the brisk trade in the catching, curing and export of fish; a man of property, wealthy enough, at any rate, to be able to pay for his son's education.

There was another more lucrative trade carried on by the Polperro fishermen at the time. Huge quantities of contraband goods, mainly spirits, tea and tobacco, were being shipped across from Guernsey and sold on for handsome profit. The risk of seizure by the Revenue vessels patrolling the Channel was more than outweighed by the rewards but the 'Trade', as it was known locally, declined rapidly after the murder of a Customs officer near Plymouth in 1798. A smuggling vessel named the *Lottery* was involved and a Polperro man named Tom Potter was subsequently tried at the Old Bailey for murder and executed for the crime. It was an episode that shocked the community and led to a gradual decline in the smuggling trade that had flourished there for decades.

The young Jonathan grew up among the fishing families who occupied the cottages clustered around the harbour in Polperro; a child with a lively and enquiring mind who was happy in his own company, and happier still exploring the tidal pools and coves along the rocky shoreline in the neighbourhood of his home. When the fishing fleet returned to harbour, he would watch fascinated as the catch was brought ashore, learning to identify and distinguish the different varieties of sea creatures. But his formal education began at the local dame school in the village where he learned to read from a horn book, a short-handled oak bat on which was placed a lesson card with the letters of the alphabet, covered by a thin sheet of transparent horn. There it was that Jonathan, seated alongside his little schoolfellows on low benches, first learned to read and write and to memorise the Lord's Prayer. Another equally enduring memory was 'the great frost' in January 1795, the year that the Thames froze over and French troops invaded Holland across the frozen waterways. 'I was then at school; and recollect that I saw a salmon which was frozen so stiff as to be capable of standing on its end. A pitcher of water also burst; and the fragments fell down, and left the water standing solid.'[1]

At the age of seven he was sent away to a boarding school in the nearby hamlet of Lansallos run by Thomas Sedgwick Cole, a small, deformed and somewhat eccentric individual who nevertheless employed the very best teachers for the 70 boys there. 'At this age I could read well and write also; for my learning amounted to this long before I left home' he was to recall later. But though he always spoke with gratitude of his parents' determination to give him the best education available, Jonathan never forgot the unhappiness he felt at being parted from them at such a young age and strongly disapproved of sending any child away to boarding school.[2] Another early memory of his time at Lansallos was of the Nore mutiny by sailors of the Royal Navy in 1797, led by Richard Parker in protest at the primitive and brutal conditions of navy life at the time. 'One of my school fellows having on some occasion uttered some seditious expressions in answer to some threatening of the Master, he received from his companions the name of Parker.' The mutinous 'Parker', it seems, was firmly dealt with.[3]

The school moved to Pelynt in 1798 where it became known as the Winsor Academy. Cole placed an advertisement in the *Sherborne Mercury* for a First Assistant who was to be 'well versed in Vulgar and decimal Arithmetic, Navigation, Mensurations &c'.[4] It was a fee-paying boarding school intended for the sons of merchants and other relatively well-off parents but within three years the number of boarders had reduced to 45. In 1802 Cole retired as headmaster and was succeeded by John Milton whom he had appointed as his assistant. When Cole died just two years later, his wife then married the new headmaster.[5] It was at the Winsor Academy that Jonathan was taught Latin by a Catholic priest, Father Arzell, who had escaped the horrors of the French Revolution by fleeing to England. Here he was befriended by the 45-year-old Cornish baronet Sir Harry Trelawny and allowed to celebrate mass in the private chapel at Trelawne, near Polperro, home to the family since 1600. 'Monsr. Arzell appears to have been an excellent man,' Jonathan wrote later. 'He used to go regularly to Trelawny to worship in the Chapel there in company with another priest to whom Sir Harry had given refuge, and whom, though himself a Protestant clergyman, he permitted to officiate in his private chapel. Through this it came to pass that Popery got introduced into the family of the Reverend Sir Harry Trelawny'.[6]

In due course Jonathan left Pelynt to go to the Grammar School at Bodmin where the Rev. Moses Morgan was the headmaster. Morgan was a mean, crafty man. Every night he would read a long extract from the Bible in a voice like the droning of a bee, and any boy who fell asleep was sent to bed without supper – much to the profit of Morgan.

It was during his time at school in Bodmin that news of the Peace of Amiens, signed in March 1802, brought with it a temporary halt to the hostilities with France that had begun with the French Revolution. Even before the treaty was ratified, the Admiralty ordered all armed ships and hired cutters to be paid off while Polperro celebrated with an 'illumination'; lights were placed in the windows of every house, a bonfire was lit at the top of one of the surrounding hills and a convivial supper enjoyed afterwards at the Ship Inn.[7] Before the peace, Jonathan later recalled, 'the invasion of this country by Buonaparte was so confidently expected that some of the inhabitants of Bodmin were almost afraid to go to bed'.

As England celebrated the lifting of the threat of invasion, Thomas Erskine, the future Lord Chancellor but then still a struggling and impecunious barrister, dined with Jonathan's headmaster Moses Morgan while he was in Bodmin on a case. Jonathan was one of a deputation of boys who asked him to persuade Morgan to give them a holiday, and this was duly granted.[8] It was Jonathan's study of Greek and Latin language and literature at Bodmin Grammar School that instilled in him a love of the classics that was to serve him so well throughout his life. The ability to read, write and dissect dead languages was the mark of a gentleman. The more he knew about ancient cultures, the better able he would be to understand his own was the received wisdom of the time.

When the war with France broke out again in May 1803, the massing of troops on the French coast raised fears that Napoleon was now really ready to invade. Not since the days of the Spanish Armada 200 years earlier had the threat been so imminent. Britain, alone and in peril, prepared for invasion. With the renewed threat, Jonathan later recalled, 'companies of volunteers were formed in all directions; and those who were not actually enrolled, had some specific duty assigned them in case of invasion: such as driving of cattle and goods, setting fire to corn, etc. Some honest hearted individuals who lived in continued fear, dreading to go to bed lest they should awake at the sound of the trumpet, or in the midst of the French troops. I recollect the painful emotion with which the French bulletins were read, the people assembling about the post office in Looe, and though it was generally concluded that they held much falsehood, yet everyone was conscious of misfortune.'[9]

There was plenty of patriotic fervour throughout Britain at the time and women in particular played an important part in maintaining morale. Jonathan witnessed both very young and very old women from villages wearing scarlet cloaks and camping out on the hills along the Cornish coast, keeping huge fires burning through the night 'to frighten away the Frenchees'.[10] One contemporary account of the subterfuge described how 'great bonfires were lit which, in the darkness, threw this army into bold relief. 'Twas camouflage. Buonaparte was expected to land with an army in Cornwall and Polperro being so strategic a centre, why not land there? So they march to and fro, looking in the distance like real soldiers guarding the coast against surprise'.

The fear was that the French would attempt a diversion by sending an army into Cornwall to draw the troops there, while the main efforts were directed against London. There had after all been several attempts to land French troops on British soil, including an expeditionary force that actually succeeded in disembarking at Fishguard, Pembrokeshire, in 1797. The Cornish, with more than 300 miles of rugged coastline to defend, felt particularly vulnerable.

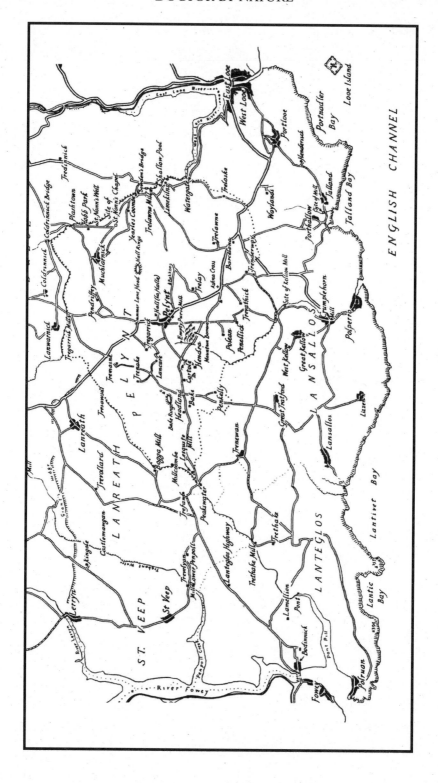

CHAPTER II

LOOMING REALITY OF WAR

Following the renewal of hostilities with France, Jonathan Couch left Bodmin Grammar School to begin a five year apprenticeship in the spring of 1804 as a pupil to John Rice, a surgeon apothecary in East Looe, four miles from Polperro. A career in medicine, backed by a sound classical education, promised good social status and the opportunity to escape the confines of his humble origins. In the daily round, he rolled bandages, compounded draughts, learned to apply leeches to the patients' skin, holding the bowl when veins were opened. Carefully observing the professional attitudes of his tutor, he came to know when people were really ill and how to handle their whims.

With the looming reality of war, Jonathan readily responded to calls for volunteers to defend the shores of England against a French invasion by joining the company of East and West Looe Volunteer Artillery under the command of Captain Thomas Bond, a lawyer and Town Clerk of both West and East Looe. As a man aspiring to professional status, Jonathan was given the rank of second lieutenant despite his youth and his commission was signed by the Lord Lieutenant, the Earl of Mount Edgcumbe, dated May 13, 1806. The volunteers' uniform was blue with red facings, similar to that worn by the regular artillery but with plain buttons. Officers like Jonathan were unpaid and expected to provide their own uniform which he did at a cost of nearly £20, including a sword with an enormous red and blue tassel attached to the hilt.[1] It was a proud moment for the teenage lieutenant when he paraded for the first time in the new livery.

An Admiralty survey of the state of the coastal defences ten years earlier had been critical of the state of ordnance at Looe: 'there was no powder in store and if the guns were in a poor state the carriages were worse, some of them unserviceable'.[2] But things had improved considerably by the time Jonathan's troop exercised the standard naval 18 pounder cannon located in the Church-end battery at East Looe as well as the nine pounders in the upper battery. Constant target practice at a mark out to sea ensured that they soon gained considerable skill in gunnery.

In all, nearly 8,500 officers and men were enrolled as volunteers in Cornwall in 1806. The Looe Artillery contingent amounted to 70. Polperro boasted an even larger troop of 200 Sea Fencibles, armed with pikes and heavy artillery and commanded by a naval officer, Lieutenant Coryndon Boger. Officially only fishermen and men whose occupation was connected with the sea could be enrolled. A considerable inducement to enrol was protection from impressment so, not surprisingly, virtually every local fisherman joined, with many a smuggler among them. 'Two hundred fine men,' Jonathan called them. The usual practice was to exercise and inspect the Sea Fencibles on Sundays so as not to interfere with their normal occupations, though some of the Methodists among them objected and were discharged.

The Looe Artillery volunteers continued until the unit was disbanded in 1809. Although Jonathan and the men under his command never fired a shot in anger, the possibility of having to do so was always present, much as it was for the Home Guard in the 1940s. The standard official instructions for the unit were 'To assemble and wait for orders'. During the six years of its existence, not a single member had died, an extraordinary record which earned the corps its nickname of 'The Looe Die-Hards'.

'During the larger part of the time of [Captain Bond's] command,' recalled Jonathan, 'an invasion from France was almost daily expected; this, and the enormous expense of paying subsidies and armies on the Continent had almost drained the country dry of its gold, so that a gold coin could not be seen in circulation for a year together, and no silver could be seen but such as had no mark either of figure or inscription'.

It was widely rumoured at the time that Jews were going around buying up as many guinea coins as possible, offering as much as 28 shillings for their 21 shilling face value; some even believed that they were acting under the direction of the Bank of England. There was concern too that, in the event of an invasion, any bank notes then in circulation would lose their value and that the Government would not be able to pay men such as the Looe volunteers. As a result, Captain Bond took the precaution of putting aside 100 guineas of his own money in gold coin for the express purpose of paying his men in order that they and their families should not suffer any hardship.

According to Jonathan, 'the result, while it excited a laugh, was unfortunate for my gallant commander. When peace was proclaimed, gold fell to its former value and this sacred deposit was no longer necessary for the intended patriotic purpose; but, alas! on examination it was found that a very large proportion of these guineas, that might have been disposed of for 27 shillings each, at least, were below the legal weight, and would now be worth no more than about 18 shillings; for which some of them were actually sold'.[3]

Captain Bond remembered the doctor in his will when he died in 1837, leaving Jonathan £3 to buy a ring or some other item as a token for having served under him.[4]

When news of Napoleon's defeat and exile to Elba in 1814 reached Cornwall, Sir Harry Trelawny's youngest daughter, Mary Harding, recorded in her diary for Tuesday, April 12, that her father 'was in raptures' and gave the family white cockades. The next day she noted: 'Heaven be praised – we shall see peace & religion restored to France'.[5]

Wellington's victory at Waterloo finally brought an end to the war and in July 1815, HMS *Bellerophon* arrived in Plymouth with Napoleon on board. Jonathan was among the crowds of sightseers who turned out in the hope of seeing the defeated Bonaparte aboard the ship lying off Rame head for two days while the former emperor was transferred to HMS *Northumberland* for his voyage to exile on St. Helena.[6]

Britain had been at war for nearly a quarter of a century and this was followed by a succession of poor fishing seasons. The maritime communities who relied on the pilchard fishing industry suffered particular hardship because their principal markets in the Mediterranean were closed to them either through enemy actions or blockade by Britain or France. Many, including the inhabitants of Polperro, alleviated this hardship by their other staple trade, smuggling. Another highly profitable sideline during the war years had been the fitting out of smuggling vessels as armed privateers, with Admiralty approval, to sail in pursuit of enemy shipping and, with luck, to seize a valuable cargo as well.

CHAPTER III

LOVE AT FIRST SIGHT

While in Looe one day during his apprenticeship with the surgeon John Rice, Jonathan happened to call on a Dr. Prynn and met Jane Prynn Rundle for the first time. It was love at first sight. Jane, then just 14 years old, was a pretty farmer's daughter with a reputation for baking appetising pastries. Dr. Prynn probably noted the young medical trainee's sudden interest and jokingly asked him if a wanted 'a good wife who could make pies'. It was not long before Jonathan was a regular visitor at the Rundle family's farm at Porthallow above Talland Bay. Jane openly confessed her love for him and he, in return, wrote letters to her almost every day, often enclosing sketches he had drawn. He was 18 when he wrote the following:[1]

East Looe. July 16th 1807

My Dearest Jane,
I have sent you all the pictures I have – some of them in a very unfinished state but it could not be otherwise at so short a notice. If these pictures are not sufficient I shall be very happy and draw some more for you.
I never can be employed more to my satisfaction than when employed in doing something for you. Did you know what pleasure your command gave me. I am persuaded that you would employ me other than you now do.

I always find I can write a longer letter to you just after I
leave your company than when I have not seen you for
some time. Was I to write at all I think a letter would not
contain it. Your charming company gives such a vigor
to my mind that I could talk for ever of you. I know of
no greater happiness than to remain always with you
– the more I see you the more I love you – this my
dearest Jane is the reason that I am always unwilling to
bid you farewell when I see you.

When I forget your kindness or love may I that instant
forget to live! I know of no happiness but what unites
in you – and I never can live without you.

You never promised to love me – the next time I see
you I shall ask that favour – and thus give you fair
warning of it.

Adieu my lovely Jane,

Yours sincerely,

Jonathan Couch

John Rice died suddenly in 1808 before Jonathan's pupilage was
completed, and he went instead to assist another medical practitioner
named Lawrence in Liskeard. In a tribute to his former master many
years later, Jonathan said of Rice: 'He never squeezed the poor, never
sought money for its own sake, was free to give, and honourable in his
dealings with his medical brethren'. Jonathan's courtship with Jane
Rundle continued while he was at Liskeard. He exchanged affectionate
letters with her regularly, and he longed to see her again.

On completion of his apprenticeship, Jonathan learned that he
had secured a place at the combined Guy's and St. Thomas's teaching
hospitals in London. It was a momentous time for the young
Cornishman. Before setting out on the three day journey by coach
to the city he spent a final few days in Polperro, taking his leave
of family and friends. While he was there, he called on Jane at her
home above Talland Bay where, in the course of a tearful farewell,
she gave him one of her bracelets and a handkerchief as a keepsake;
he, in turn, presented her with a gift of a parasol, the first to be seen
in Polperro.[2] Arriving in London in 1809 for the first time a few
days later, Jonathan found city life a stark contrast to the relative

tranquillity of the fishing village he had left behind. London was, in fact, notorious for its smutty and unhealthy air. Smoke produced by coal fires created unhealthy fogs and a poisonous outdoor atmosphere in the city. The noise was even worse. Iron rimmed wheels on cobbled pavements, carriages bumping over pot-holes, horses' hooves clattering, axles squeaking, carters, coachmen and vendors shouting, children yelling and dogs barking meant that noise was an aspect of London life which was hard to ignore. Polperro, even with its stench of fish, seemed a long way away. His darling Jane even more so.

The young medical apprentice's education had been followed with particular interest by Sir Harry Trelawny whose celebrated ancestor, Bishop Jonathan Trelawny, had been one seven bishops sent to the Tower of London in 1688 for defying King James II. Sir Harry took the trouble to provide his protégé with an introduction to Dr. William Knighton, a prominent London physician who later became Private Secretary to King George IV. Knighton was a Devonshire man who specialised in the delivery of babies and who had the reputation of being the best-mannered doctor in London; he had corresponded with Sir Harry's sister, Letitia, during his apprenticeship to an uncle in Tavistock and readily agreed to take Jonathan under his wing. Such connections afforded Jonathan swift and easy access to London society and he soon became a regular visitor at Knighton's imposing home in Hanover Square – apart from a four month period in 1809 when his host was asked to accompany Lord Wellesley (later the Duke of Wellington) on a trip to Spain during the Peninsular War.

Guy's and St. Thomas's hospitals were then located next to one another on the Southwark side of London Bridge and, like the other students, Jonathan would have been adding to the knowledge and experience he had already gained during the five years' apprenticeship he had served in Looe and Liskeard. The 18 months he spent in London, then the best-known surgical centre in the world, gave him the opportunity of seeing the very latest and most up-to-date treatments of the more serious accidents and diseases that he would have encountered in Cornwall. Moreover, the anatomy lectures and work in the dissecting room gave him much valuable knowledge and experience. As his surviving notebooks reveal, everything he learnt and saw during his time there called up memories of old patients or corrected out-of-date methods and beliefs prevalent in his home county. Among the pages of hand written notes, made both during and after the lectures he attended, Jonathan describes in graphic detail various surgical procedures adopted at the time to relieve a variety of painful and chronic conditions, in addition to a wide range of case histories.

All the lectures on the practice of medicine, chemistry, physiology and other aspects of medical treatment and diagnosis were delivered at Guy's, while the teaching of anatomy and surgery was centred at St. Thomas's where one of the greatest surgeons of his day, Astley Cooper, delivered his lectures on anatomy in the small ill-ventilated theatre. The advice given in his lectures also included his views on the general conduct of life and in particular the proper conduct of a doctor. In one of Cooper's students' note-books preserved at Guys, the following passage occurs in the introductory lecture:[3]

> 'Give me leave to remind you, gentlemen, that in your conduct here will probably depend your future rank in life. I have known at these Hospitals between three and four thousand pupils and it has been the result of my observations that universally those who were studious and attentive during their attendance here have gradually advanced to a responsible station, whilst those who were careless and idle and lounged away their time in public-houses have met with confusion and disappointments, and never been able to maintain a responsible station in life.'

Astley Cooper famously once told his students: 'If I laid my head upon my pillow at night without having dissected something in the day, I should think I had lost that day'.[4] The difficulty lay in obtaining something to dissect. At the beginning of the nineteenth century the only bodies which could be lawfully claimed by the medical schools were the few that were bequeathed for the purpose and the bodies of executed criminals. The supply was wholly inadequate for the number of students.

A description by one of Cooper's students at the time says 'he was dressed in black, with short knee-breeches and silk stockings, which well displayed his handsome legs of which he was not a little proud'.[5] Another account relates how 'he would not infrequently throw his well-shaped leg upon the table at the lecture when describing an injury or operation of the lower limb, that he might more graphically demonstrate the subject of his discourse'.[6] By all accounts, he was good-humoured, affable and extremely popular with both students and patients alike. His influence on Jonathan was immense because Cooper had a genuine love of the profession that had made him a very wealthy man. His principle was never to let anyone who consulted him leave his consulting room without giving satisfaction on the nature and proper treatment of the case. In a letter home to his father shortly after his arrival in London to begin his studies, Jonathan wrote enthusiastically: 'Mr Cooper, our surgeon, is the first surgeon in the world'.[7] Like Sir William Knighton, Jonathan's London host and mentor, Astley Cooper, was also created a baronet and was later appointed physician to George IV.

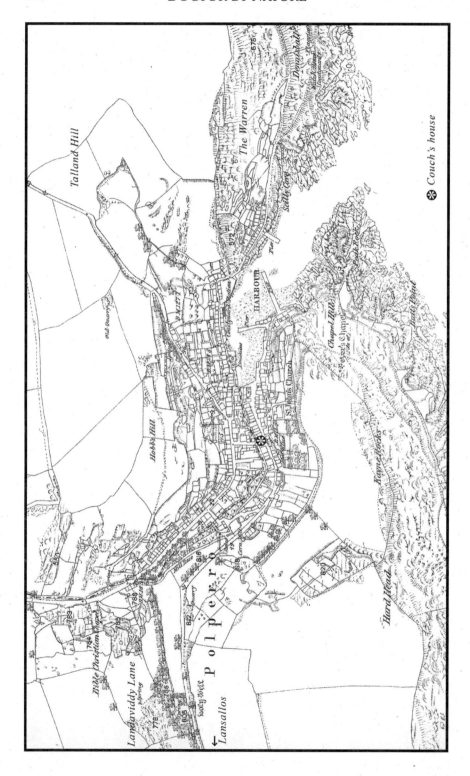

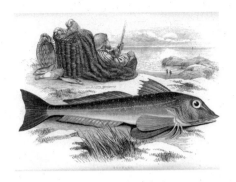

CHAPTER IV

A SUDDEN AND BRUTAL END

On the completion of his hospital studies in London, Jonathan had obtained the necessary qualifications for the practice of medicine and returned home to Polperro in 1810 where his father was now partially paralysed, after suffering a severe stroke some five years earlier. There were many who expressed surprise that such a promising young doctor should have turned his back on the many career opportunities that no doubt awaited him in London and elsewhere, choosing instead to stay in the small and remote Cornish fishing village of his birth. But 71-year-old Richard Couch, crippled with paralysis, was in need of constant care and attention and his only son was determined to remain at his side and do what he could for the father to whom he was so devoted and to whom he owed so much. And then there was his 'dearest' Jane, patiently awaiting his return.

Jonathan's passionate courtship of Jane Rundle had continued throughout his time as a medical student in London where 'her letters breathed the most ardent and constant affection'.[1] He responded by sending her gifts of ear rings, a gold chain and an ivory fan. The couple were still very much in love when, early in 1810, Jane, just 18 years old, discovered she was expecting a baby. Her parents may well have persuaded her to withhold the news from Jonathan until he had finally completed his medical studies and returned to Polperro later that year. In any event, they resolved to marry as soon as was practicable and, on Tuesday, August 14, 1810, Jonathan and Jane were married at Talland church by the curate from the neighbouring parish of Lanteglos.[2]

Walking weddings were a tradition in Polperro. The steep ascent up Talland Hill made it almost impossible for horse-drawn vehicles to be used except for the very elderly and infirm. Jonathan and his family would have set out on foot, though his father was doubtless conveyed otherwise. Meanwhile, the bride's party prepared to walk down to the church from the Rundle family's home at nearby Porthallow, headed by Jane's family and friends closely followed by the bride herself accompanied by her father, Edward, in his Sunday best. The young doctor's wedding attracted a large congregation, anxious to get a glimpse of the happy couple.

Afterwards, the party processed back to Polperro for the wedding feast to the sound of the Talland church bells pealing, Jonathan and Jane hand in hand as they made their way up Bridals Lane. As was customary on such occasions, all the boats in the harbour would be dressed in flags and bunting; when the procession came into view a *feu de joie* was fired from every available musket, fowling-piece, revolver, cannon and gun in the village.

Jonathan's father had the tenancy of three properties by the harbour in Polperro and Jonathan and Jane moved into one. From the moment he set up practice at his home at the age of 21, Jonathan Couch found a steady supply of patients who sought treatment for a variety of afflictions and conditions such as gout, tuberculosis, dysentery and hernias as well as broken bones and childbirth complications. Despite the poor living conditions of many of the families he visited, the adults were generally a hardy race of men and women but childhood diseases were all too prevalent.

At the end of August that same summer, the landscape artist Joseph Farington visited Polperro during an extended sketching tour of Cornwall. He arrived by boat from Looe, a journey that had taken two hours because unfavourable wind and tide meant rowing the whole way, and he noted in his diary:

... After leaving Looe Island there was nothing to engage the attention till the Boat approached the Harbour of Polperrow, where a scene singularly romantic and picturesque open'd to the view. Polperrow is a small fishing port, almost wholly inhabited by fishermen. It consists of a number of Houses clustered together which cover the lower part of a steep Hill which is the boundary of the head of the Harbour. They were built of stone or of mortar of various colours. The roofs are of slate. Everything that comes into view has a character of simplicity, and is in perfect unison. It is formed for the Landscape Painter.[3]

Farington, at the age of 53 one of the leading English landscape painters of his day and a prominent member of the Royal Academy, had a romanticised view of Polperro as his exaggerated engravings of the harbour reveal. An earlier but anonymous traveller who had arrived there in 1793 described the houses as 'mean, dirty & disagreeable & the inhabitants rude, stupid & uncivilized'. But neither man mentioned the overwhelming stench of fish that hung in the air and in the houses, clinging to the clothing of all who came in contact with it.

On his arrival at Polperro Farington stayed at the Ship Inn, run by Martha Rowett, a widow who had taken over from her brother, Charles Guy. Early the following Sunday he hired a horse and rode, with a local man as guide, to Fowey for the morning service. Along the way, his guide told him that Polperro had about 1400 inhabitants.

Whilst the smuggling trade was carried on money was plentiful, but that being over the condition of the people is much changed; but they live and are healthy, & few of the children that are born die. Not so in Plymouth ... where a large proportion die very young. The Fishermen & their families live upon Fish, bread & Potatoes, and never think of eating animal food, but on Sundays, & they are then the worse for it. The life of a Fisherman is not a life of hard labour, otherwise they would require animal food. The gains of a Fisherman are of course uncertain, but may be averaged at 60 to 70 pounds a year. The men & women marry at a very early age, & generally signs of connexion make it necessary for the credit of the female.[4]

Farington's observations would have been familiar to Jonathan, attending to his patients while his young pregnant wife settled happily into their new home. Away from the clamour and commotion of London, Jonathan felt at ease among the fishing folk, moving freely through the narrow streets that led round the harbour, past jowters with their panniers of fish and the groups of curious women and girls knitting outside the cottages. England was still at war with France but in Polperro the days passed peacefully enough.

On September 30, a little over six weeks after their wedding ceremony, Jonathan awoke in the middle of the night to find Jane shivering feverishly. Her condition remained unchanged for the next two or three days when she went into premature labour and on Friday, October 5, she gave birth to a baby girl. Jane's fever returned, however, and her condition rapidly worsened. Within a week she became delirious as, day after day, Jonathan sat by her bedside holding her hand and fanning her with the same ivory fan he had sent her from London until at last, in the early hours of Sunday morning, October 14, 1810, she died 'without a struggle or groan'. In spite of all his medical training and knowledge of obstetrics, Jonathan could only look on helplessly as her life slipped away. 'She was sensible to the last and though unable to speak, yet she took an affectionate leave of me. She kissed me two or three times and just before the fatal moment, when her feet, arms and face were cold, she squeezed my hand. Thus passed away the glory of this world!'[5]

At the time, Jane's death would probably have been attributed to what was then known as childbed fever. Such cases invariably resulted from septicaemia arising from infection during childbirth but in Jane's case, so graphically described by Jonathan, it is clear that the infection has already taken hold several days before she went into labour. That suggests she had probably developed a severe urinary tract infection (pyelonephritis); the resulting septicaemia would have induced her premature labour and, in the absence of prompt diagnosis and treatment with modern antibiotics, rapid death.

Even at a time of high maternal mortality during the childbirth, the death of a mother was always a tragedy. Despite being able to save his daughter's life, Jonathan was unable to prevent the death of his 'lovely Jane'. It was a swift, unexpected and brutal end to their all too brief time together. On October 16, exactly nine weeks after their wedding, Jonathan followed the coffin up over the hill to Talland churchyard, along the very route they had taken as newlyweds. After a brief funeral service led by the Rev. John Millett, curate of Lansallos, Jane Prynn Rundle was buried in the churchyard above the bay where she had spent so many happy hours as a child. Jonathan was left alone with a beautiful baby girl, named Jane after her mother, to mourn the loss of his beloved wife.

In later life, Jonathan often reflected sadly, 'In twelve months I was a young man, a married man, a father and a widower'.[6]

Exactly two years later, the grieving Polperro doctor was still mourning the loss of his bride when he wrote:

> Two years are past, since on this day, my loved wife was taken from me - time has mellowed my grief, but my regard and my regret are undiminished; oh! may that affection and care which would have been shewn thee, my love, be directed to thy dear daughter! When I forget thee, my own dear Jane, may my right hand forget her cunning! [Psalm 137] Still I feel I love her - still I mourn her loss, and ever shall. But let me not again set up an idol in my heart, as I have done; - let me love, only in submission to the divine will - ready to give it up whenever he shall call; yet this is much more difficult than can be thought by those who have not been tried.[7]

The thought that troubled him most, however, was the uncertainty of whether or not Jane had known she had received absolution before her death. As a devout Christian he would have taken steps to ensure that it was given as she lay dying in their home. Years later, another of his children recalled him saying on one occasion when speaking of Jane's death: 'She was so young that for months I was miserable, wondering about her state.'[8]

Jonathan also confided that he had had a dream in which she appeared. 'On this particular night I was lying awake in great distress, thinking that never again should I have a happy moment unless I knew of her safety. Every night for months I had experienced the same agony. Not so much grief at my own loss (although that was great enough), but the thought that there had been so little time to prepare for another world, when (I suppose I must have dropped asleep, but the vision – for it was more than a dream – was so real that I thought I was wide awake) I saw her standing by the bedside looking more radiant than ever I had seen her in life, and in a voice as clear and distinct as possible, [she] told me she was quite happy, happier than I could imagine.'[9]

The dream, whenever it occurred, appears to have put his mind at rest as he looked upon it as a divine message.' His faith was clearly a source of great strength. Baby Jane, meanwhile, was probably being looked after by her 68-year-old grandmother, Philippa Couch, among others.

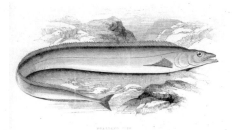

CHAPTER V

DREADFUL TIMES

Jonathan remained a widower for five long, lonely years before proposing to his second wife, Jane Quiller. She was the 24-year-old daughter of an adventurous seafaring family that figured frequently in the smuggling and privateering exploits from Polperro at the end of the eighteenth century. The prize money earned by the Quillers from the capture of valuable French and Spanish ships brought them great wealth. Jane's grandfather, John Quiller, had amassed a small fortune from the seizure of several prize vessels while in command of a privateer named the *Brilliant* in 1793, but there was a price to pay. He, her father Richard, and two of her brothers, Richard and John, were all lost at sea.

Jane's twin sister, Elizabeth, had married Robert Lane in 1812. Lane described himself as a merchant's accountant and was employed by Zephaniah Job who had acted as agent and banker for the Polperro smugglers for many years and now owned a successful merchant bank in the village. Jane's engagement to the Polperro doctor was welcome news to her widowed mother Mary.

Jane's brothers Richard and John had had the misfortune to be captured by French privateers in the Mediterranean in 1810 while serving aboard an armed dispatch vessel named the *Black Joke*, on hire to the Navy. After a spell in captivity in Algiers, they were eventually released and returned home 'in most miserable plight, having lost all except their bible,' according to Jonathan, who added: 'Subsequently they sailed together to the Island of Teneriffe in an armed merchant ship; but after leaving the island they were never afterwards heard of'.[1]

Despite the loss of so many male members of the Quiller family, the wedding ceremony at Lansallos church on Monday, June 12, 1815, was a happy occasion, attended by Robert and Elizabeth Lane and their two-year-old daughter as well as Jonathan's little daughter, Jane, now nearly five years old, and her grandparents and cousins. Once again, bride and groom would have set out on foot along the narrow lane to Lansallos, followed by the wedding guests and onlookers. If Jane's mother Mary felt any sorrow at seeing her remaining twin daughter married it would have been more than offset by the pleasure of seeing her become the doctor's new wife.

For Jonathan himself, there was the joy and companionship of a wife again. Almost exactly nine months after the wedding, Jane gave birth to a baby boy on March 12, 1816, and three months later, on their first wedding anniversary, the couple took him to Lansallos church where he was baptised Richard Quiller, taking his mother's maiden name as a middle name in the traditional manner.

When Jane's mother died the following year, the doctor and his wife and their two children, Jane and Richard, moved into the house that had long been the home of the Quiller family in Polperro. Jonathan's daughter, Bertha, described it many years later as 'quaint and picturesque both inside and out'.

> Set down on the Lansallos side, with the river for its boundary from Talland, by its very oddity it strikes the visitor at first sight. The walls, four feet in thickness, and built before line or measure were thought of, are beautiful and unique in their irregularity; so much so on the inside, that they once called forth from a local tradesman, the remark that he "would just as soon paper Peak Rocks". With chimneys of different sizes and height, and with a roof which would puzzle the greatest architect alive to name its style, the house was yet the essence of comfort, if not cheerfulness. Set so much under the western hills of the village, it loses the sun from the middle of October until the beginning of February, so that brightness and life depended on the arrangements within. The rooms, several in number, are

no two on the same level; a step up here, another down there, places the unsuspecting visitor in danger of breaking his neck. In one of the bedrooms, the one overlooking the river, are two long cupboards, one on each side of the fire-place; in these, if the floor be taken up, will be found two large recesses, deep, deep, down into the wall, which are generally supposed to have been used as hiding places during the visits of the "press-gang" as they were termed, when able-bodied men were impressed into His Majesty's service whether they willed it or not; or have served as shelter for those who were being inquired for on account of their smuggling propensities. Nearly every house, in those days, had such hiding places, where, too, a successful "run of goods" could be stored, but very few remain, unless they have been lost sight of by later generations. The room underneath was known as the "parlour", and this became Mr. Couch's sanctum, where in reality he lived, thinking, writing, and occasionally receiving visits from persons of note. Cosy, but small, an eminent visitor, once, on leaving exclaimed, "Who would think that such a small space could contain so much science?" The beams supporting the upper rooms on the Lansallos side of the house must not be passed over in silence. They consist of an oak tree, cut down, split into lengths, and laid across from wall to wall, with no regard for uniformity in size or shape, and they seem disposed to last as long as the surrounding hills, age failing to disfigure their natural beauty, or to render them unsafe as supports.[2]

It was on one of those beams in the house that a key was hung which no-one dared touch. The key belonged to the quadrant used by Jane's father, Richard Quiller, who had hung it on a nail there before setting out on his last voyage in 1796 with strict instructions that no one was to take it down until he returned. Richard, who had commanded a privateer called the *Lively* during the Revolutionary wars with France, never returned and so the key to his quadrant hung there until the house passed into the hands of a family that had no connection with either the Quiller or Couch line and it eventually disappeared.

The jubilation that had swept through England in 1815 following news of the French defeat at the Battle of Waterloo (just days after Jonathan and Jane's wedding in June) was short lived. The following year saw a particularly wet summer, resulting in a poor harvest and very little hay for winter forage.

The post-war agricultural depression was at its height when Mary Harding wrote in her diary at Trelawne: 'Dreadful times, Mr Couch said yesterday, even at Polperro the distress was universal. Those who had money thought they should never receive any more & were afraid to spend. There is no circulation of money, & the corn is abominable, many children have been killed by the complaints in the bowels brought on by the bad barley which is like birdlime more than bread.'[3]

Just a few days later, one of the worst storms in living memory battered the south coast of Cornwall during the night of Sunday, January 19, 1817. The storm, when it struck, caused immense damage and destruction in Polperro. According to the *West Briton*:

> 'A violent gale came on, this time from the south-east, and about midnight increased to one of the most tremendous storms which the oldest inhabitants recalled to have witnessed, being scarcely equalled by that which carried away the Eddystone light house many years ago ... At Polperro the ruin is terrible; out of 45 fishing boats belonging to the place, 30 have been dashed to atoms; most of those remaining are incapable of being repaired. Upwards of 60 families are deprived of pay. The pier is nearly destroyed and several dwellings and cellars have been washed away. Three new boats; all the timbers, tools, &c. which were in a shipwright's yard, have been carried away, and the adjoining dwelling house much injured. The loss to the proprietor, Mr. John Rundle, is nearly £800. The entire damage at Polperro is upwards of £6000.'

Jonathan put the damage figure somewhat lower than the reported figure of £6,000, but in the circumstances it was almost academic. In his account of the storm and its aftermath he said: 'Its direction was from the S.E. a very unfavourable point; and the sea, being driven by a furious gale to an extraordinary height, swept away a great deal of property. It covered the 'Green' from one end to the other, and reached to the top of the parapet wall of the bridge there, a height of five feet, and stopped the mill-wheel with its violence. The tide, in a body, swept over the highest point of the Peak, and, as near as the eye could judge, at double the height of the rock, not in mere spray, but in a solid body of water. The premises occupied by the Coastguard were soon levelled with the beach; the shipwrights' yard on Consona rocks, and a cellar and chamber over it, were demolished with two stop and two tuck seines [large fishing nets used to catch pilchards] there stored. About thirty large boats and a great many smaller were utterly destroyed, so that scarcely a piece could be recognised, the wreck strewing the harbour and streets. Happily no lives were lost, though the danger to many was imminent. The damage done was estimated at £2000.'[4]

The scale of the destruction was overwhelming. Despite all the sea defences constructed over centuries, including two substantial piers protecting the inner harbour, the damage was worse than anyone could remember. For the fishermen, deprived of the means of supporting themselves and their families, it was a disaster. Work began immediately on rebuilding the harbour quays, closely followed by the shipwright's yard and then, in April, repair of the inner pier, raising its height by a foot. The more badly damaged outer pier took seven months to rebuild, paid for by Zephaniah Job who had purchased the harbour four years earlier.

Job spent the last few years of his remarkable life in a cottage at Kellow near Crumplehorn mill in the coomb above Polperro. During his final illness he was attended by Jonathan until his death on the last day of January 1822 at the age of 73. Job had dined heavily the previous evening and was found dead in bed the following morning. Despite the fact that he had died without leaving a will, the man who had acted as banker for the smugglers for nearly thirty years left enough cash and property to settle all his outstanding affairs, including Jonathan's final account which amounted to £12..13s..6d.[5]

It was a busy time for the young Polperro doctor. He continued his medical rounds and even found time to contribute articles on croup (throat infections among local children were common) and 'the efficacy of digitalis applied to scrofulous sores' to the *Annals of Medicine and Surgery*, a medical journal published in London. In addition, Jane was pregnant with their second child and, in June 1817, she gave birth to a daughter, Margaret. 'A sweet babe' her father called her, but concern for her health grew when she started suffering from convulsions at an early age.[6]

Jonathan and Jane had two more children by the time his elderly father Richard, so severely disabled by the stroke that had afflicted him nearly 20 years earlier, finally died at the age of 83. In a tribute to him after the funeral at Talland in February 1823, Jonathan remarked: 'In life and death he was eminently a man of peace'.[7]

No sooner had Polperro begun to recover from the destruction wrought by the 1817 storm than another disastrous storm struck the village on November 23, 1824, washing away the new inner pier and part of the outer one, and causing other heavy damage to the harbour.

The *Sherborne Mercury* had an even more graphic report:

> 'Of the numerous boats belonging to the place only five or six have been preserved; and of the boats belonging to three pilchard seans only one has been saved. The whole amount of property destroyed by this tremendous storm is very great: two houses, with the whole of the furniture they contained, have been entirely washed into the sea, and two if not three more are so materially injured as to be wholly uninhabitable. Though several of the inmates encountered imminent danger in their endeavours to save their property, happily no lives were lost.'[8]

A committee formed to inquire into the losses suffered by the fishermen and others found that there had been loss by the destruction of piers, houses and fish cellars, quays, fishing boats, coals, salt and goods of various descriptions worth more than £2,343; in addition there was partial damage to houses and many other losses including 19 fishing boats belonging to men with no other means of subsistence, and a further five boats damaged. A few poor families whose houses were carried away in the storm had lost furniture and clothes valued at £45.[9]

The Couch family's solidly built house near the harbour had once again survived and the doctor readily agreed to supervise the employment of the poor fishermen who had lost their boats and sheds in clearing the harbour and collecting stores for rebuilding the piers. A public subscription was raised and among those at the head of the list were Sir Harry Trelawny with £30 and Jonathan himself with £5. Almost £800 was contributed.

The root of the problem of storm damage lay in the fact that the two quays built on the western side of the harbour were quite inadequate for protecting boats and buildings in a severe storm. Until the Duke of Cornwall pier was eventually built on the east side in 1861, it was not uncommon for a strong tidal surge to force its way up the narrow river, burst over the parapet by the Couches' house and flood the lower rooms. On one memorable occasion, the doctor's study was flooded to such an extent that a thick layer of sand and mud was deposited on the carpet; when the water receded, a number of small freshwater eels from the river were left wriggling about.[10]

Such storms did occasionally have an unexpected bonus however. In December 1831, after yet another severe gale had battered the coast of Cornwall, Jonathan went for a stroll along the beach near Polperro in case anything of interest had been brought ashore during the night.

'At nearly low water the tide had ebbed about fifty feet from the place where lay a flat stone on a small accumulation of sand, and on removing the sand I perceived the tail of a little fish, the body of which was concealed beneath. When removed from its hiding-place, and placed in a pool of water, it appeared new to me, although its active motions prevented for a time the distinguishing its head from its tail; but when these energetic actions ceased it fell to the bottom and remained without motion. While yet alive, the figure was drawn which now forms its portrait.'[11]

What Jonathan had discovered was a small fish-like creature called a lancelet which attracted particular attention from marine zoologists during the early part of the nineteenth century. His detailed description of the find is typical of the care and precision with which he recorded each and every item he discovered. After sketching one live specimen, he preserved it in a spirit solution and sent it to his fellow naturalist, William Yarrell, in London, while another one was later sent to the British Museum.

Yarrell was five years older than Jonathan and in 1817 he had become a member of the Royal Institution, set up in 1799 by a group of leading scientists. His first publication at the age of 40 in 1825 was *On the Occurrence of some Rare British Birds* in the Linnean Society's *Zoological Journal* and he was later elected a Fellow of the Society. His major works were *A History of British Fishes*, published in 1836 with considerable assistance from Couch, and *A History of British Birds* – the work upon which his fame largely rests – published in 1843.

By the time of that severe storm in December 1831, Jane Couch had given birth to a further four sons: John Quiller on December 13, 1818, who died just two days short of his eighth birthday; Jonathan on August 28, 1820; Thomas Quiller on May 28, 1826 and, finally, another named John Quiller on November 12, 1830. The three youngest boys were all baptised at the Wesleyan Association chapel in Polperro where their parents were active members of the congregation.

Jonathan's mother, Philippa, died a few days before her ninetieth birthday in August 1833, but not before seeing her eldest granddaughter (Jonathan's first child), Jane, married to Peter Hitchens, a farmer's son, the previous summer. The wedding took place at Lansallos church, near the bridegroom's home at Tregue, and in October of that year their first child, Richard, was born.

Philippa Couch was evidently a remarkable woman. Although her memory had begun to fail in the last few years of her life, her devoted son recorded a revealingly clinical assessment of her state of health. 'Her sight had been obtuse, and her hearing dull for many years in her middle age; but for a year before her decease, when she became subject to these wanderings of mind, her sight became so good as to enable her to read small print; and her hearing recovered much of its power. I heard her repeat from memory, with accuracy, a chapter in the New Testament, that she had learnt as a task for a prize more than four score years before. Though remarkably abstemious in regard to food during her middle life, she became acute in her appetite and digestion for a few years before her death, except for a month or two before her decease when she began to decline in health and vigour.'[12]

In his *Catalogue of British Birds* Jonathan added the following lines of verse after his mother's death at the foot of an entry for the Dabchick [Little Grebe]:[13]

Softly we lay
Our lov'd in death; yet not as death esteem'd
A gift to be return'd, a pledge redeem'd,
In God's own day.

Many people have wondered why the man who ranks with many of the greatest naturalists of the nineteenth century should have been content with the quiet contemplative life in a small out-of-the way Cornish fishing village. True, his aged and ailing father begged him to stay, but he could easily have returned to London after the death of his parents. Had he done so however he would have been cut off from the sea and the countryside he had come to know and where he felt most at home. Jonathan Couch was born to observe nature and to record what he saw.

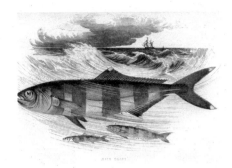

CHAPTER VI

ROOKS OF TRELAWNE

Jonathan became the much trusted medical adviser of the Trelawny family and other local gentry in the district in addition to his poorer neighbours in Polperro. He not only gained the fullest confidence of Sir Harry and the rest of his family at Trelawne, but was soon welcome there as much as a family friend as their physician, spending many hours in the well-stocked library transcribing ancient documents and manuscripts.

He attended Sir Harry's daughter, Mary Harding, as early as March 1813 and there are several entries in her diaries the following year when her husband, John Cooke Harding, was taken ill one night in early January during particularly severe weather; so severe, in fact, that the mail coach from Plymouth overturned in a snow storm on Bodmin moor. Mary's indifferent health resulted in several more visits from Jonathan throughout 1814, and on one occasion at midnight on July 1, 1816, he was called to attend her ten-month-old baby daughter, Letitia.[1]

'He brought something for her to take but it has not yet passed thro' her. Very uneasy, it is dreadful to see her in such a state. Vexed on all sides,' Mary's diary entry records. 'Mr Couch came again in the afternoon, but nothing has yet taken effect – 3 given in the evening but to no purpose.'

A week later Mary's two-year-old daughter fell ill as well. 'Theresa so very ill I do not know what to do with her. Sent for Mr Couch who, extraordinary as he thinks it, pronounced it to be a fit of the gravel [in the kidney producing colic pains]. We put her in warm water now every time she wants to p. Her shrieks are dreadful.'[2]

Both children recovered soon afterwards. When Mary's mother died in 1822, Sir Harry, already an ordained Anglican priest, went to Rome to be prepared for ordination into the Catholic Church, leaving Trelawne in the hands of Mary and her husband and with very little money to run it. Sir Harry was finally ordained as a Catholic priest in 1830 and remained in Italy until his death at Laveno by Lake Maggiore four years later.

Just before Sir Harry's death in northern Italy, the novelist Mrs Anna Eliza Bray paid a brief visit to Trelawne in November 1833 in search of material for her historical romance *Trelawny of Trelawne*. There she recalled meeting Jonathan Couch, 'a medical man of talent who lives in the neighbourhood and is a linguist, an antiquary, a naturalist and a zealous preacher among that respectable sect the Wesleyan Methodists'. A few days later the doughty authoress strode down into Polperro and called on Couch at his home where she found him 'surrounded by his books and curiosities'. He told her that in past great storms 'the sea had more than once broken in and risen to the height of three feet in his parlour, where we were then sitting. He also mentioned having seen the waves in a tempest swell, rise, and break at least a hundred feet above the spike rocks at the entrance of the harbour. What a glorious sight it must have been!'[3]

The earliest surviving portrait of Jonathan Couch, a pencil sketch dated 1824 by an artist identified only as W. Dance, shows a handsome but serious young man smartly attired in a tailored outer coat worn over a waistcoat. His shirt has the high collar fashionable during the early part of the nineteenth century, worn with a double white neckerchief. The oval lenses of his spectacles are typical of the period and were almost certainly prescribed for him.

Jonathan was 35 at the time and already well advanced with his unpublished *Journal of Natural History* which he had begun in 1805 at the age of 16, when he was in Looe, and which eventually filled 12 volumes. In it he recorded, with the same diligence and precision as his other notes and journals, his observations of birds. One of the earliest, in April 1810, was of watching a robin carrying a blade of grass to its nest, 'a day or two after the young had left the eggs. I looked at it with a spyglass'.[4] It is the first evidence that he used a telescope to watch birds.

At the time of Jonathan's birth, the number of useful books available on British birds was small. But a biological as well as an Industrial Revolution was taking shape and interest in the natural world was further increased by publication of the Rev. Gilbert White's *Natural History of Selbourne* in 1788. This work, which continues to appear in illustrated editions today, inspired more people to take an interest in wildlife than almost any other single work in the English language.

One of the books most often referred to by Jonathan in his journal was Thomas Bewick's *History of British Birds.* Bewick was a skilled artist and wood engraver, technically one of the very best, who spent seven years preparing the finely detailed illustrations of birds for his two volumes, published between 1797 and 1804. After his death in 1828 he was commemorated by having a swan named after him. Bewick presented Jonathan with a copy of his *Fables of Aesop* with its equally appealing illustrations and the two men developed a great respect for one another; on one occasion Bewick writing of Couch: 'Your labours will, I hope be a great acquisition...'[5]

Jonathan also corresponded at length with his friend the naturalist William Yarrell, both having an abiding interest in fish and birds. Jonathan rarely travelled far from Polperro, but when he made a special journey to London in August 1835 with the intention of securing a place for his eldest son, Richard, at the combined Guy's and St. Thomas's medical school, it says much for his friendship with Yarrell that he stayed with him at his home in St. James's. While he was there, Jonathan paid a visit to Guy's hospital where he spoke to Bransby Cooper, the nephew of Sir Astley Cooper whose lectures on anatomy he had attended 25 years earlier as a young medical student, about obtaining a place there for Richard.

A few days later he wrote to his wife:[6]

1835, August 31st
Ryder Street, St. James's.

My Dearest Jane,

I wrote you as soon as I arrived in town, and of course
suppose that you have received my letter to-day. It was
written in haste, and with a hand little fitted for a scrawl;
but I am now able to go about it more at my ease, and
also, I am happy to say, to give you a favourable account
of the object of my journey.

I find Mr. Yarrell exceedingly kind, and ready to take any
trouble in the objects I wish to inquire about. Our first
visit, therefore, was to Guy's Hospital yesterday, where I was
introduced to the steward, who will afford every assistance
and guidance when Richard comes up, by putting him
in the right way. I had opportunities too of speaking to
Mr. Bransby Cooper, nephew of Sir Astley, and he invited
me to call on his uncle. I saw Dr. [Thomas] Hodgkin,
one of the lecturers, and by favour of the curator of the
museum, and Mr. Daw, whose business it is to make casts
of diseased parts, I had an opportunity of inspecting
these places, usually shut up, except from lecturers and
pupils. Mr. Yarrell mentioned my name and purpose of
placing Richard with these gentlemen, and they expressed
themselves ready to notice him, which to a young man
and a stranger must be an immense advantage. Mr. Yarrell
has a nephew, now and for some time past a student at
Guy's; from him also considerable assistance and advice
will be accessible. Taking all these things together, and
more which I cannot include, I consider my journey as
highly satisfactory, and if he does not profit by it, it will
be his fault, not mine.

To-day I have been to the British Museum, and examined
it as fully as the time would allow; and here I had an
opportunity of being introduced to Mr. [John Edward]
Gray, who is in charge of a portion of the establishment.
He knew my name, and said he had been at Polperro, and
promised to introduce Richard to the more select part
of the museum. I have no doubt of his being attentive

1

A pencil sketch of Jonathan Couch at the age of 35, dated 1824,
possibly by George Dance (1741-1825).

2

An early 19th century oil painting of Polperro harbour
by the English landscape artist William Linton.

(by kind permission of Ann Pierzina-Killian)

3

Joseph Farington's engraving of Polperro harbour
following his visit there in 1810.

4

Warren Cottage in Polperro, birthplace of Jonathan Couch in 1789.

5

Guy's Hospital, London, in 1799.

6

Astley Cooper, the surgeon at St. Thomas's hospital
whose lectures were attended by Jonathan Couch.

7

William Knighton, whose London home was frequented by
Jonathan Couch as a medical student.

8

St. Thomas's Hospital Certificate signed by Astley Cooper.

9

Trelawne, near Polperro, the home of the Trelawny family.
(*Photograph by Lewis Harding c1860*)

10

Sir Harry Trelawny (1756-1834).

11

William Yarrell.
(*by permission of the Linnean Society of London*)

12

John Minards (left) and William Minards.

13

Jonathan Couch's nomination as a Fellow of the Linnean Society
signed by George Magrath, William Rashleigh and Davies Gilbert
dated 21 July 1823.
(*by permission of the Linnean Society of London*)

in this respect. I must speak, however, of Mr. Yarrell and his sister (but a little younger than himself), for they are exceedingly kind - just in the way I could wish, without giving themselves, any more than myself, trouble, except indeed that I fear I have kept Mr. Yarrell walking something more than is quite reasonable. This, however, will not happen again, or but to little extent.

And now, my dear Jane, do you endeavour to make yourself comfortable, and inform all about you that I shall certainly know whether [the children] are behaving well or ill. I shall be glad to hear from you, but in order to do this you must write immediately. I leave the greater number of things which are passing under my notice until our meeting; in fact, it would be impossible to write it if the paper would contain it. Adieu, and by way of showing how kind and affectionate your heart is, let me find on my return that you have done all that which will best make yourself comfortable; which will best gratify me.

I am, yours affectionately,   Jonathan Couch

Richard Couch duly joined the ranks of aspiring young medical students at Guy's and St. Thomas's hospitals the following month at the age of 19. Nearly three years later Jonathan proudly noted that his son had passed his examination at the College of Surgeons and received his Diploma three days before he was legally old enough to practice. Richard gained several honours including a silver medal for ophthalmic surgery and he also passed his examination at the Apothecaries Hall. He returned to the family home in Polperro and embarked on his medical career alongside his father.

Away from the carriage wheel clatter of cobbled London, Jonathan continued to receive interesting specimens of birds as well as fish for identification, given to him by his neighbours and patients in Polperro, from the well-to-do to the poorest fisher folk. He made extensive notes on the plumage and anatomy of every bird he examined, comparing them critically with Thomas Bewick's *British Birds*. Other people would describe to him unusual birds they had seen, or nests they had encountered. Two local men named in his journal are John and William Minards, cousins on his mother's side of the family.

'John is too accurate an observer to be mistaken' wrote Couch of John Minards' identification of an Alpine swift near Polperro in the summer of 1835, adding 'he might easily have shot it if he had a gun'.[7] The killing of wild birds, no longer tolerated today, was a virtual necessity in the early nineteenth century when the general rule was 'What's hit is history, what's missed is mystery'. Advances in ornithology required close examination of specimens, as Couch did, often in company with his friend Clement Jackson who kept a pharmacy in Looe. Couch rarely killed birds himself, although there is one early entry in his journal for January 1816, in which he admitted having 'kill'd some Bullfinches, which were devouring the Buds of the gooseberry; & find their gizzards to be stuff'd with the buds in a triturated state'.[8] Generally he was at pains to care for and observe the habits of captured birds that came his way, such as the wigeon that was caught by some boys in January 1836 and was kept by Couch in a cage until it died four months later, during which time he made copious notes on its growth of new feathers.[9]

William Minards was out fishing one day in May 1816 when he observed four birds landing on his boat in misty weather. They were brought ashore exhausted and released. Although Couch did not actually see them, he concluded from Minards' description that they were willow warblers. William Minards was also responsible for a more interesting account of wrens nesting habits given to the doctor in October 1835: 'on his own knowledge, that in a severe winter, these Birds have been accustomed to cluster for warmth. In one case in a hole in an hedge, where the moss abounded, he found a Cluster or ball, as large as a globular quarts measure: & in a short distance in the hedge were three or four of these clusters, all together little less than an hundred.'[10] This was the largest gathering of its kind ever recorded in Cornwall.

Ornithology was still a developing field of knowledge and precise identification of birds was often difficult, even for an experienced observer. Bewick's books were not infallible, as Couch said in his *Catalogue of Cornish Birds* begun in 1829, when he pointed out Bewick's mistaken identity of a Little Gull for a young Kittiwake.[11] This beautifully bound volume contains elaborate pen and ink drawings by him on almost every page, including one of a Little Gull shot in Falmouth harbour by Clement Jackson in 1824. Even this specimen has more recently been identified as a young Sabine's gull, thus highlighting the problem of accurate identification. Another of Couch's sketch books, entitled 'Figures of Natural Objects' begun in 1836, includes several drawings of birds' heads in which the feathers have been parted to reveal the position of the ear, as with the young Cuckoo drawn in July 1854, the 'ear opening upwards, the lower rim bony – rigid and standing out to catch the sound from above'. It was a characteristic consequence of his medical training that aroused his interest in the anatomy of animals in addition to the more prosaic observation of their occurrence. The book also contains a sketch of a Little Auk drawn on January 18, 1870, less than three months before his death.[12]

Several sightings of unusual birds occurred at Trelawne where Couch was a regular visitor for many years. A rare long-eared owl came down the hall chimney there one evening in September 1839, and nearly two decades later Couch reported: 'For more than 30 years I have seen or heard a pair of green Woodpeckers having nested in the old chestnut trees which stand in the field leading from Trelawny House to the Garden'.[13]

Lewis Harding, son of Sir Harry's daughter, Mary Harding, returned in 1846 from a ten year visit to Australia, much of it spent as a catechist at a penal settlement on remote Norfolk Island, suffering from the after effects of rheumatic fever. Like the rest of his family, he too became a patient of Couch. The doctor noted that Harding, now aged 40, 'had returned from a distant climate to Trelawny in a very imperfect state of health' and prescribed, as occupational treatment, that he should observe the actions and habits of the rooks at Trelawne, making daily records for a year from August 1847.[14]

Couch, who was then frequently to be found in the library at Trelawne working on the first volume of his translation of Pliny's *Naturalis Historia* for publication later that year, diagnosed that Harding was probably suffering from some form of nervous breakdown. The rookery at Trelawne was one of the largest ever recorded in Cornwall and Harding's diary of his observations, entitled *Life of a Rookery collected for Jonathan Couch*, remains the earliest known study of any single species of bird in such detail, achieved without the use of binoculars or telescope, much of it being done from Harding's room at Trelawne. Couch, as both naturalist and medical adviser, maintained a continuing interest in the progress of the Rooks Journal, making criticisms and suggestions, so that it can fairly be said to be a master/pupil production. Harding's detailed observations of the birds also contain several references to the political upheavals across the Channel at the time:

> 'We hear of the revolution in France, and that Louis Philip[pe] has abdicated. The moral storm has its counterpart in the physical storms here. Since last week the gales and squalls interfere with the rooks building their nests, they depart in the morning singly and gloomily, contending with the south wester. Storm continues to rage. Wind south west. We hear Louis Philip[pe] is at Neuilly on his way here on the whirlwind which distresses these rooks.'

While Louis Philippe was being driven from France by the 1848 revolution (he and his Queen were smuggled to England as 'Mr & Mrs Smith', with nothing except the clothes they wore), so too was Lewis's father, John Cooke Harding, returning to live at Trelawne accompanied by his chaplain.[15]

Couch was particularly interested in the rooks' habit of nesting close to man such as near 'an aristocratic mansion in the gothic style of building' as he recorded in his *Illustrations of Instinct deduced from the habits of British Animals*, published in the same year that Harding was observing the rooks at Trelawne. 'A Rook has been known to occupy a tree not higher than twenty feet from the ground, rather than remove to a distance from so dignified a neighbourhood: though there was no bond of attachment arising from long association of affection, for the building in its present condition is of no remote date'.[16] The old formal gardens and gate-house at Trelawne had been largely demolished on the orders of Sir Harry and fire destroyed the coach house and stables in December 1855.

Lewis Harding's study of the rook colony in the grounds of Trelawne led to an interest in photography, then still in its infancy. The earliest evidence of this is a photograph in Couch's private memoirs dated October 1856 with the caption: 'A photograph collodion likeness is taken at Trelawny by Mr Lewis Harding, as an amusement. One a positive, holding a newspaper, one a negative, full length, holding the tusk of the African Babiroussa'. Couch also added, 'Many portraits since'.[17]

The wet plate collodion process used by Harding was one of the first photographic procedures invented. Collodion, discovered in 1846, was originally used as a surgical dressing; by dissolving gun-cotton in a mixture of alcohol and ether and painted on skin, it rapidly dried leaving a strong thin film. In 1851, Frederick Scott Archer used it to coat photographic glass plates: when the collodion set, the plate was immersed in a bath of silver nitrate and then placed, still slightly moist, in the camera ready for instant exposure. The exposed plate then had to be developed immediately in a darkroom. The resultant prints had a delicacy and refinement of detail that had not been obtained before, and the new process proved to be quicker, cheaper and more certain of success although requiring considerable skill and patience on the part of the operator.

Lewis Harding's photograph of Couch shows him at the age of 67, seated by a table and holding the tusk in his left hand. It was taken at the same time as his portrait was painted by Richard Opie, an artist who had travelled from his home in Plymouth to undertake the commission for a fee of £2, with a further £1 for the frame. The cost, Couch noted self-deprecatingly, 'shows that a picture of high art could not be expected'.[18] Opie's portrait, in which his sitter is portrayed holding the tusk of a walrus, shows a man with a firm determined mouth who looks back at the painter with candid brown eyes; the initial impression is of a very neat individual of great dignity, impeccably dressed in the fashion of his youth.

Another full-length photograph of Couch by Harding around this time again shows him elegantly dressed in the fashion of George IV's time, wearing a double white neckerchief instead of the more fashionable collar and tie, and holding a stove pipe hat. His clothes were not made by the local tailor; a traveller from a London tailor made a circuit of the West Country and took orders and measurements for his suits. His shoes were adorned with broad silver buckles made especially for him out of some old crown pieces by Samuel Coad, the Polperro blacksmith.[19]

Thankfully for posterity, Couch features in several of Harding's photographs. One shows him standing at the bottom of the 'new' road just above Crumplehorn, complete with top hat and umbrella;

another more distant view of him outside his house by the Saxon bridge sees him surrounded by a group of women and children. Harding, who lived in Osprey Cottage just above the house in the Warren where Couch was born, was also on hand with his camera equipment when a Thrasher shark was brought ashore in Polperro in 1865. His photograph shows the huge fish, captured by a boat from Mevagissey, as it is loaded onto a cart in the harbour ready for Couch's examination, watched by a crowd of inquisitive onlookers.

CHAPTER VII

AGE OF DISCOVERY

What led the son of a Polperro fish-curer to become one of Cornwall's foremost natural historians? As the only child of elderly parents he was accustomed to keeping his own company; with the benefit of a good education and a natural curiosity of the world around him he had ample opportunity to indulge his interests at an early age. As a lad of 14 Jonathan watched and kept a record of the activity of a bee that had made its home in a hole in the door post of his parents' home.[1] And throughout his life he made copious notes of similar observations, many of which were included in his published books, articles and scientific papers.

Some of his earliest published work appeared in the *Imperial Magazine*, a new publication based in Liverpool whose editor, Samuel Drew, was a Cornish Methodist and friend of Couch. Launched in 1819, it was a curious compendium of religious, moral and philosophical articles and Couch was among its first contributors with *Observations on the Tree of Life*, signing himself 'Ipolperroc'. Others contributions from him followed, on such varied topics as *The Carpenter Bee and Meteorological Phenomena* in 1820 and *Authors and Books in the English and Foreign Languages which are necessary for the formation of a small and select Library* in 1821. The following year he gave an account of his own observations of the arrival and departure of birds in Cornwall including the phenomenon related to him by the fishermen of migrating birds settling on their boats far out at sea, too exhausted to reach land: 'even the strong-winged Swallow is sometimes able only to fly from one end of the boat to another'.[2]

His writing - fitted in between attending to his patients – was done in the crowded confines of the parlour at his home in Polperro which he shared with his second wife Jane and their four young children.

By 1824 he had contributed at least a dozen articles to the *Imperial Magazine* and was beginning to come to the attention of other members of the scientific community of the day. He had become particularly interested at this time in the classification of animal and plant species, an issue that had concerned the Swedish naturalist, Carl Linnaeus, in the eighteenth century. It was Linnaeus who developed the system of classifying and naming animals and plants that is still used today. He died in 1778 and the Linnean Society of London was formed ten years later for 'the cultivation of the science of natural history' and to continue the work that Linnaeus had begun.

There were obvious difficulties in identifying and classifying specimens, especially those which appeared to differ very slightly from the accepted Linnean standard. As Couch himself said, in a reference to his paper on the *Natural History of Fishes found in Cornwall* which he had sent to the Linnean Society in 1822: 'The difficulty of forming a correct opinion on this subject arises in part from the great variety observed in specimens of the same species; but more particularly from the fact that when my Paper on the Cornish Fishes was published, I could not persuade myself that the species there described could be unknown to naturalists of more extended observation'.[3]

Couch's reputation as an intelligent observer of natural history soon led to his being elected a Fellow of the Linnean Society. His letter of nomination dated July 1823, describing him as 'a gentleman well augmented with various branches of Natural History', was signed by three prominent West Country figures: George Magrath, a naval surgeon and Fellow of both the Linnean and Royal Society who had been Nelson's flag medical officer aboard the *Victory* during his command in the Mediterranean; William Rashleigh, who had been MP for Fowey; and Davies Gilbert, a former High Sheriff of Cornwall and MP for Bodmin. At a meeting at the Society's rooms in Soho Square on March 16 the following year, Jonathan Couch's nomination was approved.[4] His admission, for a fee of five guineas, meant that he was now in the company of some of the most distinguished men of the time such as the explorer and naturalist Sir Joseph Banks, the polar explorer Sir John Franklin and, the following year, Sir Thomas Stamford Raffles, founder of the Zoological Society of London and of modern Singapore.[5] It was a rewarding moment for the 35-year-old Cornish surgeon and, notwithstanding his medical and other qualifications, from that moment Jonathan Couch proudly added the letters FLS after his name.

It was an exciting time for natural scientists, a golden age of discovery of new species of animals, birds, fish and insects as well as plants, some already known but not yet classified, others hitherto unknown or not yet identified as new or distinct. And, as always with the emerging taxonomy, there was the possibility of a new genus of species being named after the person who first discovered it.

Within a matter of months, Couch was writing to the Linnean Society, enclosing a description of a tiny crab-like insect which he had spotted on the surface of a tidal pool on the shore near his home, together with a much-enlarged drawing of the creature, submitting it as a new species of the genus *Phalangium*, which included numerous varieties of spiders and mites.[6] This was followed up with another letter asking if the Society would be interested in publishing a paper on some new species of Wrasse in the Society's annual journal *Transactions*.[7]

> Polperro, Cornwall
> August 26 1825
>
> Sir,
> Having as a Naturalist more particularly directed my attention to the study of Ichthyology I have in my possession notes for a paper on the genus Labrus; in which beside more satisfactorily arranging & describing those that are unknown I have discovered & figured one or two new species. I beg leave to enquire whether it is probable that a part of the Transactions of the Linnean Society will soon be published? This enquiry arises from a desire to have this paper inserted in the next part; but should there be sufficient material already collected or should the publication be so far advanced as not to admit my communication - in either case I should be compelled

to retain it; because having been employed in making collections for a work on fish - the drawing required to illustrate the communication would be required for my own publication. It is essential to my plan to be able to refer to the Linnean Trans. already published - or to give the figures in my own work. I beg further to say, that having some time since had the honour of communicating to the Society an account of a new species of Gadus - if that Paper should be deemed worthy of publication I shall feel great pleasure in furnishing an accurate figure of the species there described.

I am, Yours very respectfully
Jonathan Couch FLS

The paper he referred to concerned a rare Scale-Rayed Wrasse, caught by a fisherman off Dodman Point on the south coast of Cornwall. It was about to be cut up for bait when the man, realising it was not a fish he had seen before, carefully preserved it for Couch who, after drawing and describing it, arranged for it to be sent to the British Museum.

These were the first of many similar submissions to the Linnean Society over a period of more than 40 years, in the course of which he had numerous papers read and published. It was customary for papers submitted by members to be read at a General Meeting of the Society, an often tedious process. Others intended for publication appeared in the quarto *Transactions*. Couch's *Natural History of Fishes found in Cornwall* was his very first paper submitted and it was accorded the rare honour of being read by the Society's founder and first President, Sir James Edward Smith, in February 1822 and published three years later. This was followed in 1838 with another paper, announcing the discovery of what Couch claimed was the first recorded occurrence of Wilson's Storm Petrel in Britain:

It is probable that the weather ... had driven to us this rare stranger, the first of its species I believe on record as having occurred in Britain, which was found dead in a field at a few miles from Polperro, and was brought to me for examination. As our Sailor Boys were in possession of numerous living specimens of the Stormy Petrel, which are taken with great facility when the weather suits, I found no difficulty in instituting a comparative examination of these two species.[8]

There is only one recorded instance of Couch attending a meeting of the Linnean Society. In 1849, in the course of one of his rare visits to London, he spent two weeks as a guest of his friend and fellow naturalist William Yarrell at his home in Little Ryder Street, St James. Together they attended the annual meeting of the Society at the Freemasons Tavern near Covent Garden. It was chaired by the Bishop of Norwich, Edward Stanley, who, Couch noted, 'lays no claim to depth of knowledge on scientific subjects, but as Chairman he knew how to unbend, and render himself agreeable, not to say facetious'.[9] Yarrell, who had been elected a Fellow in 1825 a year after Couch, was unanimously elected Treasurer of the Society at the meeting and his portrait hangs today on the stairway leading to the library at the Society's premises in Burlington House, Piccadilly.

The 1849 visit was an especially memorable time for Couch who was introduced to many of the leading scientists of the day by his friend Yarrell. He dined on more than one occasion with Professor Thomas Bell, the Guy's surgeon who was later President of the Linnean Society when Charles Darwin first presented his evolutionary theory to the Society in a joint paper with Alfred Russell Wallace in 1858, followed shortly by publication of his *Origin of Species*. Darwin's book, which presented the idea that natural selection was the mechanism of evolution, changed the prevailing view of biology for ever.

Couch and Yarrell, dining with Professor Bell, were joined by Professor Richard Owen, an anatomist and palaeontologist who created a name for himself as a controversial but brilliant scientist, who rejected Darwin's theory of evolution. Couch wrote:

'I found Mr Owen to be an open hearted man, free to communicate, and without the least appearance of assumption. His absolute acquaintance with physiological subjects and comparative anatomy is apparent on the slightest enquiry and is known to Europe. It was amusing to notice the antagonism between him and Mr Bell on the political topics of the day; Mr Owen being a Liberal and Mr Bell a Conservative. The latter is distinguished by his good nature, which is so well known by his friends, that the reason of the long delay in the publication of the portions of his Crustaceans is ascribed to his readiness to be diverted from his course by any request made to him. In physiological knowledge on recondite subjects he readily yielded deference to Mr Owen. The conversation at table was highly interesting, diversified, but never dull or trifling, and my only regret was my want of memory to carry away the substance of it'.[10]

Among other distinguished men Couch met during his stay with Yarrell were Robert Brown, the Scottish botanist who had accompanied Matthew Flinders on his voyage to chart the coast of Australia; Dr John Edward Gray, the keeper of zoology at the British Museum who he had met on his 1835 visit to London; Sir Henry de la Beche, the director of the Geological Survey of Britain; Edward Forbes, Professor of Natural History at the Museum of Practical Geology and his colleague Robert Hunt, keeper of mining records at the museum; and John Joseph Bennett, of the British Museum and Secretary of the Linnean Society. Some had previously corresponded with Couch and no doubt they were as keen to meet the Cornish surgeon-apothecary of whom they had heard so much as he was to meet them.

Couch had just published details of a new species of mackerel in the *Zoologist* journal and it is very likely that there would have been some discussion about that among the members of the Linnean Society in Couch's presence. The carefully preserved fish had been sent to him by his friend Clement Jackson, the apothecary in Looe where it had been caught in July 1848; after drawing it and noting its distinctive spotted markings, Couch sent it on to Yarrell for his opinion who agreed that it was indeed a new species and should be named *Scomber punctatus* or Dotted Mackerel.[11] It was just one of many exciting discoveries by the Polperro doctor that brought him to the notice of the wider scientific community.

When Yarrell had published his *History of British Fishes* in 1836, he had been generous enough to acknowledge that much of the information in the book had been provided by Couch. This was indeed true, for Couch had given Yarrell an entire manuscript to use as he thought fit. It would be impossible to calculate how many hundreds of hours of observation, dissection and writing are contained in this manuscript which is now in the library of the Linnean Society in

London. The leather-bound volume contains many illustrations by Couch, some of fishing vessels and others of different species of fish, including several exquisitely coloured drawings. The opening page has the following inscription:

> *This volume was employed by Mr Yarrell in the Composition of his History of British Fishes: being the same that is quoted in that work, by the name of Couch's M.S.*
>
> *Jonathan Couch*
> *Polperro 1836*
> *September 23rd*

By way of introduction, Couch begins: 'Of all the Departments of Natural History none has received so little attention as Ichthyology, and in the science of Political economy, no part has been so little studied as that of the Fisheries altho' their great national importance is generally admitted.'[12]

Couch's friendship with Yarrell lasted for many years until Yarrell died suddenly from a heart attack at the age of 72 while on a visit to Great Yarmouth in 1856. His death was a great blow to Couch who wept unashamedly on receiving the news and wrote, 'I feel the loss much and fear I am not likely to find another like him: unassuming in habits and knowledge: ready of access, and to communicate: a good physiologist, as well as general naturalist'. When his friend Clement Jackson also died suddenly that year, Couch remarked, 'His death may be said to close my intimate connection with Looe, as no one there besides cares much for Natural Science'. Greatly saddened by the loss of two friends with whom he had shared so much knowledge of the natural world, he added the following melancholy lines in his private memoirs:[13]

> *Unhappy he who feels the blow,*
> *Whose eyes have wept o'er every friend laid low,*
> *Dragged lingering on from partial death to death,*
> *Till dying, all he can resign is breath*

CHAPTER VIII

WESLEY'S LEGACY

Jonathan Couch remained a life-long adherent of the Wesley brothers' evangelical style of religious observance, often at odds with the established church of the day. But when John Wesley brought Methodism to Polperro for the first time in 1762, the dogged old evangelist got a mixed reception. 'An abundance of people had found the way thither,' Wesley wrote in his journal. 'And so had Satan, too; for an old grey-headed sinner was busily cursing all Methodists, just as we came into the town'.[1]

Such an isolated community was fertile ground for Methodism, not least because the nearest parish churches (at Talland to the east and Lansallos to the west) were two miles away and not easily accessible, especially to the elderly or infirm. Disenchantment with the established church was growing throughout Cornwall and many fishing, farming and mining communities were attracted to the simple message of the Wesley brothers. Jonathan's grandmother, Margaret Freethy, was one of the first converts of John Wesley and her son Richard, Jonathan's father, joined the Methodists at a very early age.

Wesley's first visit was followed six years later by a second in September 1768 when he arrived on horseback in the pouring rain at the home of John Rommet in the Warren. Rommet, a keen Methodist as well as a fisherman and fish-curer, had extended an invitation to the great preacher to stay overnight at his small cottage overlooking the harbour. The smell of fish stored in the cellar below proved too much however. An entry in Wesley's journal records: 'the room over which we were to lodge being filled with pilchards and conger-eels, the perfume was too potent for me, so that I was not sorry when one of our friends invited me to lodge at her house'.[2] The invitation came from a Mrs Martin to stay at her house in Talland Street and no doubt Wesley was glad to escape the stink of desiccated conger eel.

Writing nearly 100 years later, Couch recalled the enduring memories of Wesley's visits: how on one occasion he preached at a house called Way's End, standing on the level platform reached by the flight of steps which led to the second storey of the building. Another time he addressed the people from what was termed an orrel, a sort of wooden balcony on the second floor that had an open window closed by a wooden shutter.' The orrels have long since disappeared but, according to Couch, the house used by Wesley was in the Green, belonging to the blacksmith Samuel Coad, 'an energetic supporter of the new sect' and the first local preacher.[3]

Despite the pervading odour in John Rommet's house, it remained for many years the abode of visiting Wesleyan ministers as well as being used for their meetings until a decision was taken to build a new meeting-house on a site in the middle of the village on the Talland side of the brook. The initiative came from Zebedee Minards, a neighbour of the Couch family, whose wife Mary had left the sum of £5 to be given to 'some charitable purpose' following her death at the age of 50 in 1789. Zebedee agreed to double the amount and when Jonathan's father Richard was told, he promised to double whatever Minards contributed.[4]

From these small beginnings the project grew. By 1792 a 'large and respectable chapel was built' and still exists today, though probably much altered, as a schoolroom adjoining the later chapel completed in 1816.[5] The seats in the meeting-house were simple forms without backs, and men and women sat separately in rows on either side; high-backed seats were added later and arranged more conveniently as family pews. Membership of the Polperro chapel grew steadily from 51 in 1804 to 63 five years later so that, though originally quite small, the meeting-house was soon enlarged to twice its former size and in 1816 was further extended and improved by the addition of a large gallery.

The artist Joseph Farington made the following note in his diary after his visit to Polperro in 1810:

'A considerable proportion of the inhabitants of Polperrow are methodists. They assemble together to the number of perhaps one hundred on Sundays at 7 in the morning, sing Psalms, and several will rise in succession and make extempore prayers, they have no Methodist preacher at their morning meetings; but at their meetings in the evening of Sundays, they have one, persons of this description going... like Excisemen from place to place to officiate in this capacity... Methodist meetings do not affect the people with respect to the Church, to which they go regularly'.[6]

The Anglican Church had become complacent and corrupt, living luxuriously on its tithes and endowments, as it had for more than a century. Ecclesiastical affairs in both of the parishes that divided Polperro at the beginning of the nineteenth century were far from satisfactory. The rector of Lansallos, the Rev. Henry Pooley, was largely absent, employing a succession of poorly paid curates to conduct services there while still continuing to collect annual tithes from the hard-pressed farmers and fishermen. And the vicar of Talland, the Rev. Nicholas Kendall, preferred to live several miles away at Lanlivery where he was also parson, paying a curate to serve the parishioners of Talland. In the summer of 1812 Kendall employed a curate named Thomas Whitmore who conducted church services with dignity, baptising babies, marrying couples and burying the dead. But then, towards the end of the year, the new curate suddenly disappeared taking with him whatever valuables he could carry from the vicarage. Not even the news of the murder of the Prime Minister, Spencer Percival, that same year caused a greater sensation in Polperro.

Once it was known that the curate was not what he claimed to be, several couples who had been married by the 'Rev. Whitmore' came back to be married again, tormented by the thought that the first ceremony was invalid and they were 'living in sin'; and the parents of eight babies baptised by him also brought them back to be baptised a second time. The 'Rev. Whitmore' turned out to be an impostor by the name of Robert Peacock who was eventually convicted of fraud and hanged at Gloucester gaol in September 1814. Jonathan

Couch, aged 23 at the time and still grieving the loss of his first wife
Jane, reflected the shocked mood of the parish community when he
commented: 'There must have been great laxity somewhere, or such
an imposture could not have been allowed; but we cannot fail to be
astonished at the daring of a man who could cover his frauds with
the sacred vestments of the Church, and thus recklessly scandalize the
holy calling of a minister of the Gospel'.[7]

The incident merely served to encourage the now flourishing
Methodist congregation in Polperro. A new lease of the Polperro
meeting-house was granted to Jonathan Couch and Edward Hocken
by the lord of the manor of Killigarth, who just happened to be
Nicholas Kendall, the vicar of Talland, held in trust for the Methodist
Society. A register of births and baptisms, kept from 1818, shows that
the parents' occupations included fishermen, sailors, a shipwright,
an innkeeper, a shopkeeper, a carpenter, a blacksmith, a shoemaker,
a schoolmaster, a farmer, a couple of coastguard men, a solitary
member of a higher social class – a Lieutenant in the Royal Navy, no
doubt also attached to the Preventive Service; and, of course, Jonathan
Couch himself.[8]

Even at this stage there was by no means universal acceptance of the
Methodists whose teachings discouraged many of the pleasure-loving
appetites of the fishing community. One local preacher at Polperro
named Richard Geake was sometimes followed by 'large mobs, with
dreadful threats; but the Lord preserved them'. Geake, a St. Germans'
man, had married Elizabeth Langmaid, daughter of a Lansallos farmer,
in 1790 and the couple settled in Polperro. Elizabeth had joined the
Methodists at the age of 22 in 1784 and often went with the preachers
to new places; at that time she was 'the only respectable young female
in the parish who gloried in the grace of Christ'. She attended chapel at
Polperro regularly, driving or riding the three miles from her father's
house on a pony. Elizabeth had first married a sea-captain named
William Sargent in 1786 but was left a widow with a baby daughter
when he was drowned in a storm off Land's End. When she remarried,
her new husband Richard Geake became an active member of the
Polperro Methodists, holding prayer meetings and a class there. Two
years later however, Geake had the offer of a tannery at St. Germans
and the family moved there, but his grandson Edward was later to

become a close friend of Couch (and sat by Couch's bedside during his severe attack of bronchitis in 1867).[9]

Early in 1828 old Zebedee Minards died at the age of 89. Instrumental in founding the Polperro chapel, he had been born at almost the same time as Jonathan's father Richard and the two men remained lifelong friends as well as Methodists for more than 60 years. After the death of John Rommet, in whose house Wesley had preached on his second visit, Zebedee had provided hospitality for the travelling preachers until eventually age prevented him from keeping open house. Towards the end of his life he became very deaf, but remained active in good works until his last illness and, although he had outlived almost everyone of his generation, he must have been sadly missed in the village. But while 1828 saw one of the periodical revivals of religious enthusiasm in Polperro, things were astir. A sect called the Bible Christian Church, an offshoot of the Wesleyan Methodists, had already established themselves at Polperro and in 1831 a preacher from yet another splinter group, the Primitive Methodists, addressed a gathering at the Market House.[10]

A serious schism broke out among Methodists in England in 1835 when Dr. Samuel Warren, a prominent figure in the movement, led a breakaway faction calling themselves the Wesleyan Methodist Association in protest at his expulsion for opposing the foundation of a theological seminary. In Polperro, Couch joined the protest by leading a substantial group of 37 people who seceded from the main Methodist congregation in 1837 to set up on their own.

For the first 12 months they met in a room over the old market-house on the Green which they named (as did similar groups elsewhere in Cornwall) the Refuge. The list of members of the new Association group included members of many of the best-known families in Polperro, including Minards, Quiller and Langmaid. They were divided into four classes: one, led by Couch, met on Tuesdays; another, led by Thomas Peake, met on Fridays; a third, led by William Magor (brother-in-law of William O'Bryan who founded the Bible Christians), met on Wednesdays, and the fourth, led by Henry Langmaid, met on Sundays.[11]

A public meeting was fixed for October 31, 1837, but as the little group of seceders had not yet found an adequate meeting-place, they arranged to hold it in the old Methodist chapel where all previous meetings of this kind had taken place. The wound had not yet healed however and Edward Hocken, one of the trustees of the old chapel, hit upon a way to thwart the rebels without having to do so openly. He wrote to the superintendent preacher of the old Methodists, Benjamin Carvosso, and asked him to come and preach at the Polperro chapel on the evening that the public meeting had been arranged. Carvosso duly came and began preaching at 6pm. When the rival group discovered this, they went to the minister of the little Independent chapel in the village who not only lent them that building but spoke at the meeting, chaired by Jonathan Couch.

The new Association soon obtained a plot at the foot of Talland Hill for a chapel of their own. Led by Couch, it was all planned in a businesslike way. In January 1838 seven members were appointed to form a committee to manage the project which was funded largely by shares allotted to members. The chapel – which for a century or more was still referred to as the new chapel – was a much bigger building than the earlier ones, but took only months to build. It was opened on Tuesday, September 25, 1838. Three sermons were preached and 'the congregations were very large, and the collections good', reported the *West Briton*. One of the preachers was the Bible Christian leader, William O'Bryan, in a demonstration of solidarity at a time when the Association and the Society from which it had sprung were still at loggerheads.

In January the following year the shareholders met in the new chapel and agreed upon 12 people to serve as trustees to settle the future management of the chapel affairs: Jonathan Couch, surgeon; John Giles, tailor; John Perry, shoemaker; Francis Hicks, mason; Thomas Congdon, smith; Joseph Andrew, carpenter; John Quiller, shoemaker; Richard Mutton, mason; George Coath, gentleman; John Lord, farmer; Richard Hicks, shopkeeper; and William Magor, farmer. Couch was appointed president of the chapel for the ensuing year. The list of the shareholders in 1839 was headed by Couch himself, with shares numbered 1 to 13; he later acquired a further 15, five of them from his son-in-law, Peter Hitchens.[12]

Some of what we know about the early Methodists can be gleaned from the often fulsome obituaries in the religious magazines of the period. There is plenty of evidence that nonconformity, and in particular Methodism, was almost universal in Polperro in the early nineteenth century. Small wonder therefore that leading Methodists married one another. When the Wesleyan Association chapel was licensed for marriages in 1840, the very first marriage to take place there was performed by Couch himself when he officiated at the wedding of John Blake, a farmer from Landrake, and his bride, Grace, the daughter of William Magor, one of the chapel trustees. The following year, the couple brought their baby son, William, to be baptised by Couch, as were the children of several other families between 1842 and 1844.

If no visiting preacher was available, then the doctor would readily address the congregation. Never from the pulpit, but from his pew just under it, often with his arm around each of his little daughters who would be kneeling or standing on their seats facing the congregation and holding the Bible or hymn book for him while he read.[13]

A rich vein of piety runs through much of Couch's writing. He firmly upheld the doctrine of natural science or 'natural theology', believing the universe to be full of evidence of intelligent design and proof of the existence of God. In his *Illustrations of Instinct,* published more than a decade before Charles Darwin's *Origin of Species,* he explored the intrinsic nature of instinct in the behaviour of animals, both domesticated and wild, and discussed their intellectual ability in relation to human beings. The book sought to explain the many curious habits of animals that he and other naturalists had observed. Couch knew that birds migrated from one part of the globe to another in search of a warmer or colder climate; he had noticed the way some birds would carry a snail to a stone in order to break open the shell and had watched a dog crack open the shell of a crab in the same way.

It was a first attempt to make comparative anatomy and comparative psychology illustrate each other as well as to distinguish between the instinctive behaviour of animals and that of human beings governed by reason. 'In this, then, consists the universal, decisive and permanent difference between the spiritual nature of man and animals; and its fruit is necessarily seen in his faith in God.' In other words, it was man's belief in God that distinguished him from the rest of the animal kingdom; his 'propensity to a progressive rise in intellect and purity', as Couch put it.[14] Unlike some leading members of the scientific community of the day, not even publication of Darwin's *Origin of Species* in 1859 could undermine his resolute belief in the divine purpose of nature and he would to go to his grave with his faith intact.

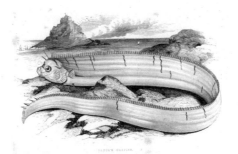

CHAPTER IX

REFUSAL TO BURY

In spite of all the demands of his patients and his tireless pursuit of natural history, Couch never neglected his family. When his mother Philippa died in 1833 he and Jane still had their daughter Margaret and their four sons, Richard, Thomas, Jonathan and John at home in Polperro with them, while his eldest daughter Jane and her husband Peter Hitchens were living near the hamlet of Lansallos.

Four years later, Couch gave his daughter Jane and son-in-law a dilapidated property near the fish market in Polperro that he had inherited from his father. Peter Hitchens spent the next six months rebuilding the house so that he and Jane, their young son Richard and baby daughters Jane and Mary Elizabeth could live there. But in 1839, shortly after the birth of their fourth child Hannah, the couple sold the house having accepted an offer to move to Brenchley in Kent, leaving six-year-old Richard behind with grandfather Hitchens at Tregue farm and three-year-old Mary Elizabeth with the Couch family.[1]

Within a few years, the couple made a brief return to Cornwall, Jane having given birth to two more daughters and Peter suffering from tuberculosis. Despite Couch's best endeavours to save him, Peter Hitchens died at his parents' home at Tregue on May 20, 1846 at the age of 37, leaving Jane with six children to bring up on her own. TB, or consumption as it was then known, was a deadly disease for which there was no known cure at the time. Only a few months later Jane's

eldest daughter, also called Jane, contracted the illness that had killed
her father. Arrangements were made for young Jane to move into the
Couch household so that she could be nursed and attended there by
her grandfather, but after eight months of coughing and fever she too
died in June 1847 - just a few days short of what would have been her
twelfth birthday.

The tragedy brought the extended Couch family all together for
the first time for several years, Richard having moved to Penzance
in 1844 at the age of 28 to set himself up as a medical practitioner.
Arrangements were made with the rector of Lansallos, the Reverend
William Rawlings, for Jane's body to be interred in the same grave
as her father in the churchyard there. And so, on June 16, 1847, the
funeral cortège set off from Polperro up Landaviddy lane for the
church at Lansallos.

On arrival at the church, however, an extraordinary scene ensued
when they were greeted with the news that the vicar could not conduct
the ceremony because no certificate from the Registrar of Births and
Deaths at Lerryn had been produced. The Registrar concerned had
long insisted that someone who was in the room at the time of the
death should travel to Lerryn to sign the register in person. Couch
had complained several times that such a demand was unreasonable,
especially as getting to Lerryn from Polperro involved a journey of
more than seven miles along a road that was both rough and steep;
on more than one occasion he had even threatened to refuse to send
his certificates there because of the inconvenience caused. He had
nevertheless taken particular care to send his granddaughter's death
certificate to Lerryn by special messenger but the Registrar still refused
to issue the necessary certificate for burial.

The Rev. Rawlings was adamant. He would not conduct the funeral
without the Registrar's certificate being produced. No amount of
pleading and protests from Jane's grandmother, Hannah Hitchens,
or Couch himself would change his mind. His only response was: 'I
can't and I won't'.

Rawlings retired to the vicarage and the coffin was defiantly
carried into the fourteenth century church, followed by the family
and mourners who processed round the interior before congregating
around the grave outside. A short service of prayers was conducted by
Couch, a function that he was familiar with having officiated at the

Wesleyan Association chapel in Polperro; three verses of a Wesleyan hymn were sung and Jane's coffin was lowered into the grave.

News of the vicar's refusal to bury the doctor's granddaughter created widespread anger and indignation locally. A full account of the incident was sent to the Bishop of Exeter who returned a polite acknowledgment but little more was heard. Couch meanwhile was urged to pursue the matter as a private grievance, a course he was reluctant to take, preferring instead a public investigation by the Bishop. Charles Walcott, a Royal Navy captain living at Portlooe, informed the Bishop that he would withhold the sum of £300 he had collected for repairs and improvements to Talland church until the matter was resolved. In the face of such pressure, a commission of inquiry under the Church Discipline Act was set up. Rawlings pleaded guilty to a charge of refusing 'to bury the corpse of Jane Rundle Hitchens which was brought to the church or churchyard of the said parish to be buried on Wednesday, the 16th day of June, of the present year'.

In mitigation, the Rev. Rawlings maintained that he had acted in sincerity, believing that 'it was his duty to refuse to perform the ceremony when no certificate from the Registrar was produced'. Had he done so, he would have been liable to a penalty of £10. On retiring to the vicarage at Lansallos to verify his decision, he said, he realised he was mistaken and returned to the churchyard where he found the coffin interred and the mourners singing hymns over it. He added that when he then offered his services they were refused. He also told the Bishop that he had offered to wait in his house until the certificate had been obtained from Lerryn.

Couch later indignantly recorded: 'Mr Rawlings was not ordinarily civil, he never made his appearance, never expressed regret at being obliged to perform a disagreeable duty, and positively never offered to wait until a message was sent to Lerryn. If he ever reperused the Act is uncertain; but he never returned to the churchyard and offered his services; consequently there was no opportunity of refusing them; which indeed he had no right to do. The verses, not hymns, in the plural number, were sung before the body was laid in its resting place, not afterwards, and consequently this part of the story is false also'.[2]

A little more than six weeks after Jane Hitchens' burial, the Lansallos vicar also refused to bury the body of a ten-month-old baby boy named Charles Henry Curtis unless his parents could produce the Registrar's certificate, prompting Couch to add that 'the allegation that [he] had changed his opinion ... is as false as all the other parts of the plea'.

The hearing at Exeter lasted for several days in October. The Bishop, Dr. Henry Philpotts, finally delivered his judgement, 'deploring' the excuse put forward by the vicar for not conducting the burial. The Rev. Rawlings was admonished 'not to offend in like manner in future' and ordered to pay the costs of the proceedings. Couch judged it 'a slight penalty', especially as it was the same that had been pronounced in a recent case involving the vicar of St. Breward for being drunk and using 'profane language' in Bodmin. Infuriated by what he regarded as Rawlings' 'decided falsehoods' he wrote to the Bishop to place on record his view of the matter in the hope that his letters would be preserved in the Bishop's Registry at Exeter.

'I believe that in his refusal to read the burial office, Mr. Rawlings had no intention of finally declining it, but only to give great trouble, and then to consent, as if by great condescension. Our proceeding to do without him certainly was what he did not expect'. Couch added that when the undertaker, John Rickards, had spoken to the Rev. Rawlings at the time, the rector remarked that 'Mr. Couch has been very troublesome'.[3]

The whole incident, so deeply upsetting to the bereaved family, made Couch resolve to establish a private burial plot on a small piece of land he had acquired at Mabel Barrow, a little over half a mile up the lane from Lansallos church. 'It is my intention that in this place I and mine shall, in God's good time, be laid to mingle with the Earth'.

Couch eventually achieved his wish, establishing a Methodist chapel alongside the little burial ground. When, ten years later, his second wife Jane died a few days short of her 67th birthday, she became one of the first people to be interred at the Mable Barrow cemetery in 'a grave prepared so as to receive another inhabitant'.

Jane Couch had been unwell for several years before her death on Sunday, 6th September 1857. On the day after her death, Couch wrote to his son Thomas in Bodmin:[4]

Monday morning
1857 Sep. 7.

My Dear Thomas
We are - I am - in great affliction - Your mother became ill
on Friday - of Malaena and although apparently better on
Saturday yesterday it returned. With her previous weakness
what could be expected. I trust in God she is with him in
Christ - leaving me - alone - to bear it as I can.
God bless you, I hope he will strengthen me.

Jonathan Couch

Thomas wrote later that his mother was 'a home-keeping woman of
simplest habits, who passed through life quite noiselessly as far as the
world outside was concerned'.[5] She had lived all her life in the same
house in Polperro and in all probability she died in the same room
in which she had been born. A tall, black-haired matronly woman
with a fair complexion, according to Thomas, she inherited all the
heat of her famous Quiller blood when roused. Jane disliked leaving
home, seldom went to Plymouth and only occasionally visited her
son Richard in Penzance, although she did go to Fowey in September
1846 when Queen Victoria arrived in the port with Prince Albert
aboard the royal yacht *Victoria & Albert* and visited the town.

Jane's only daughter, Margaret, endured poor health for most of
her life, having suffered since she was very young from the convulsions
that, according to her father 'ruined her nervous system'. By the time
of her mother's funeral she was quite ill and a little over four months
later, at the age of 40, she also died and was buried alongside her
mother at Mabel Barrow. Left alone with his remaining sons, Couch
stoically recorded, 'when her mother from failure of her own health,
thought of what Margaret might have to encounter through the
remainder of her life, her wish was to see her go into the grave before
her. And although not literally, yet providentially, so it is. Praise be
to God.'[6]

Shortly before Jane's death, Couch began keeping another more
private journal. In his distinctive hand, he inscribed the first page:[7]

Memorials
of the family of Couch
noted by Jonathan Couch

Underneath, he added a small sketch of a fist grasping a bunch of grass, adding the words, 'hand grasping Couch grass'. On the next page, headed Memorials, he wrote:

'All the world is ready to laugh at the silly vanity of those who let it appear that they are actuated by the pride of Family; and yet it has been observed, that no one is free from a feeling of this nature but such as have no family to be proud upon.

'It seems at least a natural feeling, to desire to know who were our ancestors; and if we notice the care with which this subject is noted in the Sacred Scriptures, we must conclude that it is something of which we need not be ashamed.

'Another consideration influences me. I have had means of information which if passed by, must be lost for ever, and when it is recollected that the public have no concern with this, but that it is written solely for the use of my Children, every consideration of vanity seems sufficiently obviated.'

His self-deprecating comments disguised a genuine pride in his family and forebears; several pages of the private memoirs are devoted to snippets of family history which he intended to be preserved for posterity. His grandfather Couch, he noted, was also named Jonathan, the youngest of 12 brothers all of whom except himself left Polperro to settle elsewhere. The Polperro family not only extended back to Elizabethan times, but had also acquired a modest amount of property over the years which was passed down to his father Richard.

Subsequent pages of the Memorials recall several incidents that were 'illustrative of the slow progress of improvement' in his home village. Tea had been brought ashore as contraband by the smugglers in the eighteenth century but Couch remembered his father saying that when he was boy the spout of a tea kettle was washed ashore to the bewilderment of everyone, though some thought it might have been the bowl of some strange sort of tobacco pipe. He distinctly remembered the first occasion that an umbrella was seen in Polperro: it had been given to the landlord of the Ship Inn, Charles Guy, by Carteret Priaulx, one of the Guernsey merchants who supplied goods to the Polperro smugglers, on a debt collecting visit to Cornwall in 1805.[8] And Couch himself had introduced the first parasol there, a gift to his first wife Jane during their courtship in 1809.

Much later still, in 1867, Couch added the following verse under the heading 'A memorial of my life in Polperro':

'Twas filial duty first that fixed me here:
To soothe a father's wish with heart sincere.
An aged mother next my cares engage:
To watch her comforts in extreme of age.
Then over all a Providence presides,
That snatched my joys away, and yet provides
Successive comforts still to calm the breast,
And bid the wandering wishes sink to rest.
To vacant hours He offers Nature's stores
Abounding on our rich but unsearched shores:
The forms, the habits of the sea born race,
Unknown the larger portion, find a place
In diligent enquiry: 'till at last
They fill the vacant hour, not idly pass'd.
In all his works I trace the hand of God,
Nor more in living Nature than the rod
Of his chastising hand; but more than these,
His care has fixed my dwelling, where to please
My kind preserver is my highest bliss:
And what a high reward I find in this!

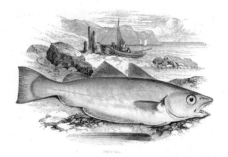

CHAPTER X

CORNISH ICHTHYOLOGIST

The marine life along the coast of south Cornwall provided the richest source of material for Couch's pursuit of natural history study throughout his life and it is no surprise, therefore, that he became known as the Cornish Ichthyologist. Flying fish, sharks, whales and, rarer still, a four horned trunkfish ventured far enough north to be caught by Cornish fishermen.

The Polperro fishermen provided him with a steady supply of specimens, some of which were quite unknown to the scientific community at the time. If anything was taken in the nets or by line at sea that they thought the doctor might be interested in, it would be kept alive and brought to him as soon as the catch was landed. Once inside the surgery, Couch would quickly mount the fish on a piece of apparatus that he had specially invented for the purpose, with a jet of salt water that played on the scales to keep the specimen fresh while he sketched and coloured it, taking great care to copy the fresh brilliance and delicate hues before the colour faded to drabness.

Couch had considerable regard for the fishermen, describing them as 'a hardy race of men, often leading a life of no little peril and privation. They are brave and intrepid, and in cases of shipwreck, or distress at sea, have been seen to run great hazard, when the prospect of danger was great, and of gain very little'.[1] He took particular trouble to instil in them the importance of accurate observation and they, in turn, took pleasure in bringing specimens to him, especially if they turned out to be something unusual. And even when the young sons of the fishermen brought him their captures as well, they were rarely dismissed without some reward or encouragement, whatever the value of their finds. 'If I don't pay them for what is worthless, I shall never get anything worthwhile,' he would say.[2]

Pilchards had been the principal harvest for generations as huge shoals would arrive off Cornwall in the summer and autumn months. Until the end of the eighteenth century, drift nets were used to catch pilchards but eventually a more complex system called seining was adopted at Polperro a few years before Couch was born. The seine was a huge net, usually a quarter of a mile in length, deployed by a boat at each end and hung vertically in the water. As soon as a shoal was encountered, the ends would be drawn together to enclose the fish. In a good season, catches amounting to several millions of pilchards were landed by a single seine unit. As well as providing a plentiful supply of food for the families of the fishermen during the long winter months when their boats were unable to put to sea, there was a thriving export trade to be had with Italy. That is, until the wars with France that followed the Revolution of 1789 prevented British merchant ships from operating safely in the Mediterranean. When peace was eventually restored in 1815, the pilchard harvest remained disappointingly small for several years. But for many Cornish men and women, the arrival of the pilchards was seen almost as an act of divine providence; Couch himself said in an essay on the *Natural History of the Pilchard*, 'It has been a subject of wonder and thankfulness in the minds of those who have learned to see a God employed in the affairs of his Providence, that this assemblage of creatures takes place within the reach of human effort at seasons when they are in the best condition to minister to human wants'.[3]

Other species of fish were usually caught by hook and line, including conger eel; conger pie was a popular dish in Cornwall as was conger douce, a cured and dried version otherwise known as sweet conger which, when grated and made into soup, was regarded as a particular delicacy. It also provided a valuable export trade to the Catholic countries of the Mediterranean. Conger eels were known to grow to enormous size; according to Couch, some exceeded 120lbs in weight and were capable of inflicting nasty

14

Jonathan Couch seated by a mounted specimen of a scorpion fish.
The microscope was manufactured by Vincent Chevalier,
the first to use chromatically corrected lenses.
(*Photograph by Lewis Harding*)

15

Lewis Harding's photograph of Jonathan Couch at Trelawne,
holding the tusk of an African wild pig in October 1856.
(*Photograph by Lewis Harding*)

16

Richard Opie's portrait of Jonathan Couch at Trelawne,
in October 1856.

17

One of Couch's drawings (Bubalis) from his
Fishes of the British Islands.

18

Title page of Couch's 'Natural History of the Fishes of the United Kingdom' which was used by William Yarrell.
(*by permission of the Linnean Society of London*)

19

A crowd of women and children gathered outside Jonathan Couch's house in Polperro. Couch can be seen standing by the doorway.

20

Jonathan Couch's house in Polperro today.

21

Richard Quiller Couch, Jonathan's eldest son,
holding an early form of stethoscope. His jacket appears to be
that of Staff-Surgeon of the Duke of Cornwall's Rifle Volunteers.
(*Photograph by Lewis Harding*)

22

Thomas Quiller Couch, Jonathan's second eldest son.
(*Royal Institution of Cornwall*)

23

Pages from Lewis Harding's 'Life of a Rookery' showing the site of the rookery at
Trelawne and the number of nest built on 11 March 1847.

24

John Quiller Couch, Jonathan's youngest son.

injuries. He recalled one instance of a fisherman who had hauled a large conger into his boat when the fish snapped at and caught his foot in its jaws before it sprang overboard, taking the man's shoe with it.[4]

Just occasionally, an observant fisherman would catch something that was of exceptional interest, as in May 1840 when what was at first thought to be a common whiting was hooked by a Polperro man but which, on closer examination turned out to have a number of features that differed from the whiting usually caught off Cornwall. The fish was brought to Couch who described it in precise detail, adding 'even to this ordinary observer, its difference from the well-known Whiting was apparent'.[5] After he had drawn and painted it, he brought it to the attention of his old friend the naturalist William Yarrell in London. Yarrell included the Polperro fisherman's unusual catch in a later edition of his *History of British Fishes,* giving it the scientific name Couch's Whiting.

Couch always observed facts without theorising. One particular fish that was highly valued for food in the nineteenth century was the John Dory, but little was known about what it fed on. From his dissection of several specimens brought to him, Couch learned that the Dory fed on pilchards, although in the stomach of one adult fish he found 25 flounders, some two and a half inches long, which led him to conclude 'we may judge that the Doree is ready to take the hook; but to ensure success the bait should either be alive, or made to imitate a living fish'.[6]

As he dissected fish, Couch took great care to ascertain the structure of their parts, often making hundreds of small drawings of their bones and joints.

On Wednesday May 8, 1850, a whale measuring over 14 feet in length became entangled in the mackerel drift-nets of a fishing boat belonging to Polperro. Unable to free itself, it eventually drowned. Held fast by both its head and tail, it was towed back to the harbour where the crew hauled it up onto the beach below the pier for Couch to examine. After carefully measuring it and drawing a detailed sketch of the creature, he identified it as a young Pike-headed whale (*Balaenoptera rostrata*). It wasn't the first encounter with a whale in the area (a 20-foot Pilot whale had been found on Looe Island just eight years earlier), but little was known of cetaceans found in British waters at the time and it naturally merited an article in the journal of the Penzance Natural History and Antiquarian Society a few weeks later.[7] Couch later sent a report on 'species of Whales which have been observed on the coasts of Cornwall' to the Royal Cornwall Polytechnic Society in which he stressed the importance of fishermen 'communicating to any competent observer the occurrence of a specimen that might not otherwise be known to him' and 'refraining from mutilating it until an examination of it has been made'. The preservation of an unknown or rare specimen of whale, he added, could well prove more valuable than the price that might otherwise be obtained from the sale of oil extracted from the carcase.[8]

Couch's son Richard was secretary and curator of the Penzance Society and continued to assist his father's study of fish whenever opportunity allowed. Within four months of his arrival in the town in 1844, Richard wrote to his father to tell him that the very first time a trawl-vessel operated from Penzance in July, a large number of rare boarfish had been caught in the net.

> 'A trawl has been established here within this last week & from it I have procured a large quantity of very fine corals & judge my surprise on finding a pannier full of the Boar Fish. I counted them & found they were sixty in number, & the man told me several others had been thrown overboard. I measured several & found them to vary from five inches to 7. I brought some home & compared them with Mr Yarrell's figure & description.'[9]

The introduction of trawl fishing raised immediate concerns with both Couch father and son however. It was particularly disliked by the Cornish fishermen using lines, nets and traps who complained that trawling cleared the sea bed of fish spawn and immature fish, ruining their bait beds and often sweeping away their drift nets, long lines and crab pots. Richard was becoming increasingly alarmed at the effect on the delicate ecology of the sea-bed, describing trawling as 'one of the most objectionable forms of fishing ever devised... not only because it is sure of catching all fish and destroying the crabs, but from the immense number of minute cods, hakes, whitings, haddocks etc. which it destroys'.[10] Trawling had already inflicted considerable damage to the conger fishery in Cornwall and there was talk of imposing a limit on fishing for crabs and lobsters to preserve stocks; the first indication of the quotas that were to follow over a century later. But the trawl fishermen themselves were invariably opposed to any restriction. As Richard's father once said of them: 'Tenacious of their rights, and firmly attached to old customs, they are not easily persuaded to adopt improvements, even when these obviously recommend themselves'.[11]

Matters came to a head in 1863 when the subject was debated in the House of Commons and a Royal Commission set up to look into the complaints against trawling. One of those demanding the enquiry was Henry Fenwick, the Liberal MP for Sunderland, who referred to the evidence of Jonathan Couch, 'one of the first naturalists in the country', in the ensuing parliamentary debate:

'The witness lived in a fishing district, and had paid great attention, for a number of years, to the subject of trawling. He [Couch] stated that: Since the practice of trawling has been introduced into this locality [Cornwall] it is the expressed belief of the fishermen that the produce of the fisheries has greatly fallen off. The destruction of the spawn, spawning ground, and food of young fish is well known; but precise evidence of this could scarcely be obtained, as all this mess is swept overboard at sea; and as many, perhaps most, of the proprietors of trawl vessels live on shore, being sailors, sail-makers, and fish merchants, the actual fishermen may be afraid to acknowledge the truth of the case through fear of being dismissed from employment. It is well known that fish caught with a trawl are much inferior in value to such as have been taken with a line, as might be supposed, when we consider that they have been dragged along the bottom of the sea for several miles amid a mass of rubbish. Their fins thus become torn and their bodies bruised, so as to become putrid long before such as are caught in any other way. I have seen surmullets caught in a trawl, that, for a time, I could hardly tell what sort of fish they were. It is my opinion that much of the injury inflicted may be obviated only by limiting the time when the trawl may be employed - that time being when the more valuable kinds of fish are engaged in spawning, and at other times they should not come within a given distance of land. I have heard it remarked, by those who are well acquainted with the subject,

that the practice of trawling is as adverse to its own prosperity
as to the fishing by hook and line, since for one fish carried
to market many hundreds are destroyed; so that trawling itself
must end at last by its own acts. But this is poor consolation
to the public, who, now that the railroad could convey them
rapidly and cheaply, might be supplied abundantly, if fish were
as abundant as formerly they were.'[12]

The three members of the Commission toured the nation, visiting
86 fishing communities and taking over 1,000 pages of evidence from
many hundreds of witnesses. One of the Commissioners was the
zoologist Thomas Huxley, then only 38 years old but already well
known as 'Darwin's Bulldog' for his robust defence of Charles Darwin's
theory of evolution by natural selection. Huxley probably had strong
views on fisheries before he embarked upon his marathon tour. He
certainly had them by the time the Commission reported three years
later, for the enquiry came to a most extraordinary conclusion that
few could have imagined at its commencement. The Commissioners
overwhelmingly rejected the contention that the supply of fish was
diminishing.

Having spent three years listening to so much evidence on
fisheries 'of the most conflicting character', the Commissioners
might have been forgiven for thinking that there was little a
government could do to improve fisheries through legislation.
Their conclusion was as shocking as it was simple: 'We advise that
all Acts of Parliament which profess to regulate, or restrict, the
modes of fishing in the open sea be repealed; and that unrestricted
freedom of fishing be permitted hereafter.'[13] The Government
acted on many of the Commission's recommendations and the
ensuing legislation effectively created a free-for-all in sea fishing
activities.

The legislation caused even greater concern to Cornish fishermen
using traditional drift nets when it was learned that coastguard officers
were to be given powers to seize the boats and nets of anyone founding
using a drift net within two miles of the shore. Couch organised for
petitions signed by the fishermen to be sent to the Board of Trade in
an attempt to amend the legislation. 'Not only will the families of
the fishermen be afflicted with great loss,' he wrote, 'but the county

of a kind of food that is of general use among us, and is the chief subsistence of the poorer classes'.[14] The reduction in the traditional harvest of pilchards in Cornwall was being blamed by many on the increasing practice of trawling. Ultimately, the 1868 Sea Fisheries Act kept the trawling and drift net fishermen apart by requiring trawl boats to keep at least three miles from those using drift nets. But many more years were to pass before there was any real attempt to conserve fish stocks and restrict the amount of fish caught.

After his marriage to Lydia Penneck Pearce, the daughter of a local magistrate, in 1853, Richard Couch set up practice from their home in Chapel Street, Penzance, where four of their children were born. Like his father, he contributed many articles to scientific journals, some about mackerel, crustaceans and the development of the frog as well as continuing his geological searches for fossils in Cornwall. But he was also a devoted and dedicated mine surgeon who was very concerned at the poor health and high mortality rate among the miners in West Cornwall where, in 1857, he found that the average age of the miners was only 28 and a man of 40 was already an old man. 'To see the men from such mines arriving at the surface after eight hours' work is a most sickening sight', he observed.[15]

Richard's own life was tragically cut short at the age of 47 in 1863. He died of pneumonia following a period of ill-health, the result of septicaemia contracted from one of his patients in the course of performing an operation a couple of years earlier. When his condition suddenly worsened in April, his father hurried to Penzance where he remained for two weeks but, despite the best efforts of his family and fellow physicians, nothing could save Richard.[16] As an alderman of the town, he was given a ceremonial civic funeral attended by the Duke of Cornwall's Rifle Volunteers (he had been their Staff-Surgeon). According to a newspaper report of the occasion, 'Most of the principal shops of Penzance were closed during the progress of the funeral cortege'.[17] Lydia was expecting their sixth child at the time, a daughter born posthumously in November and named Frances. To add to Lydia's sorrow, baby Frances too died after only 15 months of life.

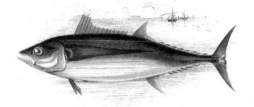

CHAPTER XI

FAMILY TRADITION

Three of the five sons that Couch's second wife Jane had borne him followed in their father's footsteps and became successful medical practitioners. Of the other two sons, they had lost one boy at the age of eight, and the other, Jonathan, suffered epileptic convulsions in childhood that left him mentally impaired. Under the care of his father, however, Jonathan appears to have led a relatively normal life at home, even to the extent of being able to assist with simple tasks. But a clue to his condition can be found in the enumerator's note in the 1881 census which refers to him brutally as 'Idiot from Birth'.

One after the other, three sons went to London as medical students in what became almost a family tradition. First Richard in 1835, then Thomas in 1849 and finally John, the youngest, in 1859. There is more than a hint of what influenced their chosen vocation in one of Thomas's later memoirs:

> 'My father one day with very little preliminary talk told me that he intended to bring me to his own profession and presenting an indenture asked me to read it and sign it. This without much consideration I did and so my line of life was taken. I had been accustomed to a doctor's life. After some manual and routine work, and with evenings spent over Latin and Greek translations the time came for me to be transferred to Guy's

Hospital where my father and elder brother Richard had been before me. A raw country lad I had much to learn.'[1]

Thomas Couch was an accomplished artist and his lecture notebooks from his time as a student at Guy's Hospital were filled with sketches, some of his lecturers and fellow students, others of anatomical or botanical subjects. His lecture notes, with headings such as 'Hernia', 'Diseases of Women', 'Induction of premature labour' and 'Smallpox' are interspersed with fragments of verse and notes on well-dressing and other ancient traditions.[2]

In a letter home to his parents in October 1849, Thomas gave an account of his day as a medical student: 'my time from 10 in the morning till 5 in the evening is fully occupied at the Hospital and the remainder of my evening serves to arrange and amplify the notes I make of the lectures'.[3]

Thomas, like his older brother Richard, attended lectures on surgery given by Bransby Cooper. 'Though not quite the lecturer his uncle (Sir Astley Cooper) was,' wrote Thomas of Bransby Cooper, 'he is still a good one, and very facetious on occasions. He gave us a rather cruel recommendation today. He advised those who had the opportunity to perform surgical operations, as the tying of the main arteries, on the lower animals'.[4] One wonders just how many medical students were encouraged to practice their surgical skills on some unfortunate family pet.

After passing his examinations as a Licentiate of the Apothecaries Company and at the College of Surgeons in 1852, Thomas spent six months at Guy's as a dresser under John Hilton, regarded as the greatest anatomist of his time. Affectionately known as 'Anatomical John', his grasp of the structure and functions of the brain and spinal cord was far in advance of his contemporaries. The duties of a dresser were equivalent to those of a house surgeon today, but were more likely to involve attending to accidents and cases of hernia, extracting teeth and bleeding patients.

Thomas and his father were close friends, often exchanging letters with their news and views on a variety of topics concerning natural science of one sort or another. The following letter from Thomas, written from his London lodgings shortly before he qualified as a surgeon apothecary in 1852, is typical:[5]

6 Union Square
June 5 1852
Horsemonger Lane

My dear Father,
I sent you at length the figure of the Dolphin. These are other
sketches of the cranium, etc. but the skeleton also shows &
perhaps sufficiently its vaulted character. [a description with
measurements follows] This is from the description of the
figured animal soon after it was taken out of the water drawn
by Mr. Reinhardt, Zoologist to the Galathea expedition.
There are some curious papers appearing in Frazer by an
anonymous hand on the archaeology of Fish & fishing. I see
the Magazine at the Coffee house where I dine & if there should
be anything especially worthy of notice I will copy it.
I have just been to the water colour exhibition with a student
whose mother is an artist & consequently had free admission.
I also visited the Royal Academy and was much pleased,
although there is no work of very special note excepting a
marvellous painting of a cathedral interior by Roberts. There
are several works of the school termed pre-raphaelite, wonderful
in manipulation but so far outraging taste, only to excite pity
for the great talent misdirected. There is a picture of this class
'Ophelia' which represents her floating in the brook into which
she has fallen from the willow. The accessories are so minutely
painted that I could recognise & name all the flowers growing
on the banks as the purple loosetrife, forgetmenot, duck weed,
etc.
I hope soon to go to the Brit. Museum. At all events I will not
forget when I get an opportunity. You received the two or three
small sketches I sent though I do not recollect your naming it.
With love to all,
Yours truly,
Thomas Q. Couch

Thomas encloses some sketches for his father of the skeleton of a
Ganges River Dolphin that had been brought back to England by a
Danish vessel named the *Galathea* in 1846. At the Royal Academy in
Piccadilly he was clearly impressed by David Roberts's interior of the
cathedral at Seville and less enamoured of the work of the emerging
Pre-Raphaelite artists, despite being able to identify all the flowers

shown in John Everett Millais' painting of Ophelia. Four days later, his father writes back from Polperro.[6]

My dear Thomas

Your two drawings came yesterday – only a little pressed together in the post & therefore not injured. The Gangetica Dolphin is evidently a separate Genus: but in the figure of the skeleton there are two defects which might lead a student of Natural History into mistake. One of these is the omission of the Pelvis: an omission usually found in skeletons, & often also in engravings. It arises from the very slight attachment which the pelvic bones have to the vertebra; but in Laughrin's very good skeleton of our common Porpoise he has preserved these bones and fastened them to their proper place; and thereby enabled one to discern an error in the usual account given by naturalists of the structure of the neighbouring bones. What may be called the brim of the pelvis is formed of cartilage & therefore is commonly lost in setting up the skeleton; but Laughrin has preserved this also. Another defect in your skeleton is the absence of what forms the substance of the tail. It is true this is also cartilaginous; but it is important as a representative of hinder extremities & Laughrin has preserved it. It gives me a better idea of the moving forward of the Cetacea than any description has been able to do. Our knowledge of the Cetacea on the whole is slight and imperfect: out figures commonly very bad & hence it is instructive to get good ones – even of species we shall never see.

Your other figures came safely – and I believe they were acknowledged at the time. They are very satisfactory.

I am glad you have been so well employed in your dressership: it will help your knowledge very much. But I think we may ascribe the Dyspepsia which you mention in your former letter to the close Confinement by day and night: & therefore in addition to any medicine you may use, I would recommend your being in the open air as much as you can, during the time you are free from

the closer Hospital duty. It is easy to treat instruction in
some hope or another, with amusement & this attention
to your health: & attention to the latter is of importance,
even in respect of your professional improvement.

Yours   Jonathan Couch

What is perhaps most revealing about Couch's reply to his son
is the extraordinary attention to minute detail, even to the extent of
appearing critical of Thomas's efforts to produce an accurate sketch
of the skeleton. He refers to similar drawings by William Laughrin,
the Polperro coastguard who assisted Couch with his study of marine
life and fossils. And he adds a fatherly word of advice to his 26-year-
old son to get more fresh air as a cure for indigestion.

Like his father and elder brother Richard before him, Thomas
spurned all offers of a hospital appointment in London after
qualifying and returned instead to assist his father in Polperro. He
was able to gain some useful experience on his own in Penzance
by acting as locum to his brother when Richard and Lydia spent
their honeymoon in London in June 1853.

The matter of a permanent position for Thomas came to a head
two years later when Couch was contacted by Nicholas Kendall, the
MP for East Cornwall, to say that he had something to offer Thomas
which he believed 'would be to his benefit'. Coincidentally, a letter
arrived a couple of days later from Edward Campbell, a surgeon from
West Looe who was home on leave from India where he had held a post
with the East India Company. Campbell's letter informed Thomas
that he had just been appointed Deputy Inspector of Hospitals with
the Turkish army under British command in Crimea and that he was
offering Thomas an appointment as a surgeon there. The position
carried with it a salary of £1.10s a day for at least one year, longer if
the war with Russia continued, and for a further six months at the
end of the year or the end of the war.

Such a salary would have been at least four times what a
young surgeon apothecary could expect to earn in Cornwall at
that time and the offer was obviously an extremely tempting one.
But newspaper reports of the wretched conditions endured by
both troops and medical staff in the Crimean peninsula since the
outbreak of war in 1853 were creating growing alarm at home;

more soldiers were dying from cholera, typhus, typhoid, dysentery, and scurvy than battle wounds. Couch was understandably concerned that Thomas would not be able to endure the hardship that such a posting carried. 'He is not able to bear hard labour, or great disturbance of rest; he is not tough, and at the end of the time he would be as much at a loss for a permanent settlement as now, with perhaps a shattered constitution'.

Father and son arranged a meeting with Kendall who explained that the offer he had in mind for Thomas was a position as assistant to his brother-in-law, John Ward, a prominent Bodmin surgeon. Although the salary of £100 a year was considerably less than what might have been earned in Crimea, a horse, medicines and instruments were provided. The prospects were good, with the promise of a partnership after ten years, and Thomas duly accepted the offer. Only a matter of weeks after arriving in Bodmin, he found himself in charge of the county lunatic asylum there during the temporary absence of the resident physician, Dr Theodore Boisragon.[7]

Thomas married 21-year-old Mary Ford at her home village of Abbotskerswell in Devon eight years after settling in Bodmin as what had by then become known as a general practitioner. Just nine months later, in November 1863, Mary gave birth to a son at their home in Fore Street, Bodmin. Arthur Thomas Quiller Couch was duly baptised the following January, the eldest of Thomas and Mary's five children.

Under the pen name 'Q' that he adopted in later life in the course of a distinguished literary and academic career that was to earn him a knighthood, Arthur wrote affectionately of his grandfather Jonathan: 'As a doctor his care for the sick was exemplary and taken for granted by all (often without reward) as his efforts to improve the conditions of his people and to safeguard the fishermen's lives never ceased'. And of his father Thomas, he wrote: 'Many have told me, while he lived and since, that his presence in a sick-chamber filled it "with a confidence that was half a cure"'.[8] Some of Thomas's friends maintained that he would have achieved even greater fame had he become a professional artist instead of a doctor.

Thomas's youngest brother, John, was an altogether less amiable character. He, too, followed in his father's footsteps to Guy's Hospital, having spent a year as an assistant to William Rendle, another Polperro born surgeon, in London in 1856. Rendle had just been appointed Medical Officer of Health for St. George's parish in Southwark and became notorious in his native Cornwall for thundering denunciations of the appalling state of the sewers in Liskeard. One of his letters to the *Cornish Times* in 1858 ended with the comment, 'I am glad to get out of Liskeard and pity my friends there'.[9] When John Couch eventually qualified as a surgeon apothecary in 1862, he moved to Penzance and set up a practice in Chapel Street near his brother Richard and family. Following Richard's unexpected death the following year, John gave his widow Lydia some help with her financial affairs but, in due course, the two quarrelled and they fell out.

John never married and lived alone in Penzance until his death in 1900. His will was disputed by Lydia Couch's three daughters and the matter eventually went to a High Court hearing the following year. John was described in court as 'a man who could hardly be described as very amiable or good-tempered ... he was somewhat vindictive'. It was also said that he had taken 'a very great dislike' to many of his relatives.[10]

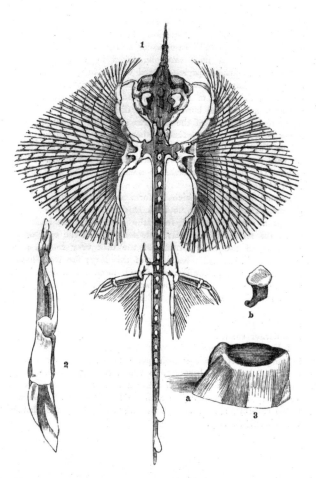

1.—Skeleton of Thornback Ray.　　2.—Skeleton of Male Clasper of Thornback Ray.
3.—Superior view of the eye of Thornback Ray;
a, the anterior part; *b*, the pedestal of the eye.

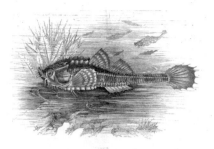

CHAPTER XII

A DEADLY DISEASE

In June 1836 Couch was called to attend a man named Thomas Broad who had suffered traumatic injuries to his left leg and thigh as a result of standing near a cannon that burst as he fired it. His injuries were so serious that Couch at first feared he would die from heart failure unless the limb was amputated, but Broad refused to undergo such a drastic surgical procedure. At a time when anaesthetics were still largely unavailable, the risk of death from amputation, either as a result of shock, blood loss or infection was considerable, even in the hands of a physician as sensitive as Couch.

Thomas Broad's condition deteriorated steadily and he lay in agony until, ten days after the accident, he finally consented to having his leg amputated. Couch duly set about the operation, working quickly as he cut through the flesh, ligaturing the arteries and sawing through the already broken femur before cauterising the stump's raw surface to stop the bleeding. The entire procedure would have probably lasted only a few minutes but, despite everything, he was unable to save Broad's life.

'The cause of his sinking seemed to be that the cellular membrane of the whole thigh, and abdominal muscles of the same side of the body (the left) had become gorged with pus, probably from inflammation,' he wrote in his Medical Journal afterwards. 'This was not perceived until the incisions had been made; when the purulent matter flowed freely and continued to drain for some considerable time; a doughy feeling of the ligaments subsiding at the same time. Amputation gave him the only chance for his life, but it was delayed too long'.[1]

Such an operation, performed without any effective anaesthetic, would have been harrowing for patient and surgeon alike. The amputation of such a limb carried a mortality risk of about 50 per cent, a depressing figure to be sure. But even a 50/50 chance of survival was a fair gain over an almost certain death without such treatment.

Such severe injuries necessitating drastic surgery were rare but accidents were common in rural life, typically injuries to agricultural workers from hay-knives, scythes and tenterhooks. Then there were accidents with guns and falling objects, such as the case of nine-year-old Benjamin Magor who was killed by a falling elm tree on his father's farm at Lansallos Barton in March 1836.[2] So too were injuries associated with horses, usually from falls while riding. But much of Couch's surgical skill would have been spent dealing with abscesses, broken bones, dental extractions and leg ulcers, the latter especially common among younger unskilled workers.

While the threat of disease was never far away, particularly among the poorer families in the neighbourhood, by and large the health of most people seems to have been surprisingly good, in spite of crowded and unhygienic living conditions. One of the most dreaded diseases was smallpox, which caused disfigurement, blindness and death. Isolated cases occurred in Polperro from time to time, and even Couch's eldest son Richard contracted a mild form of it as a medical student in London after being vaccinated early in 1836. But, in December 1837, Couch became aware that he was dealing with a much more serious outbreak in the village. Many of his patients and their families had already been vaccinated by him as a precaution against the disease, although it was still only some 40 years since the Gloucestershire physician, Edward Jenner, had first observed that a mild dose of cowpox produced immunity against the more deadly smallpox.

To prevent it becoming an epidemic, Couch at once set about inoculating as many of his patients as possible. The method used involved dipping ivory points in the lymph from the pustule of someone who had been vaccinated with cowpox about a week earlier and then inserting them into a scratch on the skin, usually between the thumb and forefinger. The recipients all developed smallpox but, with one or two exceptions, in a much milder form than the naturally-occurring disease, producing far less facial scarring and no loss of life.

> 'All that were inoculated took the infection in the first application and all have done well. Several also came under my care that had taken the natural disease and all these also had the disease mildly. Although much of this may be ascribed to the influence of a favourable season, yet I think it probable that much also may be ascribed to the favourable nature of the lymph employed and to the constitution of the boy from whom it was taken. Some of the children had emaciated constitutions: some with disorders of the skin, but these things had not a very decided effect on the quantity of the eruptions or degree of fever... In many children that had been vaccinated formerly and whom I inoculated for the satisfaction of their friends, the pustules rose in the arms, but instead of merely arising and then dying away when the constitutional symptoms might have been expected they rose fully with evident fever, but in no case did anything further follow. It was however a greater trial than I ever before saw from this operation. In no case have I overseen smallpox with eruption produced by such re-vaccination... I had before come to [the conclusion] that the power to resist the inoculated disease is no absolute proof of a like capacity to resist the natural infection.'[3]

Couch's own record of the outbreak, and the steps he took to prevent its spread, mentions a small number of cases where patients he had vaccinated subsequently contracted smallpox. One of them involved a young child that had been inoculated at the age of three weeks belonging to Thomas and Jane Bate who farmed at Kellow. Another was Thomas Braddon, a 33-year-old Polperro innkeeper who had also been vaccinated as a child; Couch noted that he 'had the disease smartly: but this partly to be ascribed to exposure to rather severe wet, windy weather when getting disordered and then to obviate the shivering, drinking 3 wine glasses of raw spirit'. Braddon's wife, Ann, did not contract the disease however.[4]

Jenner's discovery in 1796 had already proved effective in preventing the scourge of smallpox but there were many opponents to the practice of vaccination, some even suggesting that the human body might take on some cow-like characteristics after inoculation, and it was many years before any legislation was passed to make it compulsory. The 1837 outbreak in and around Polperro resulted in a total of 286 men, women and children being inoculated by Couch and a further 150 vaccinated, proof that he was in the forefront of medical practice. The fact that virtually the whole of Polperro trusted their doctor to do something that even Parliament was uncertain about is ample evidence of the confidence he enjoyed. It was a common saying there that 'if Dr Couch gave a patient up, it was no use to call anyone else in, you might just as well curl up your toes and die'.[5]

Smallpox was not the only disease with a potentially deadly outcome. An outbreak of scarlet fever near St. Austell in the summer of 1836 was unwittingly carried to Polperro by John Lord, the 15-year-old son of John and Elizabeth Lord who kept a grocery store in Lansallos Street. Although the lad himself had never contracted the disease, his younger brother George displayed symptoms of it after a week, followed by his two-year-old sister Agnes ten days later. Agnes soon died from a severe chest infection though Couch believed her death was more likely to have resulted 'from being placed in her cradle in a draft of air' rather than the scarlet fever.[6]

Epidemics of other childhood diseases such as whooping cough, measles and croup regularly occurred among Couch's younger patients; fatalities were mercifully rare but, only a few weeks after little Agnes Lord's death in Polperro, a little girl named Priscilla Johns died of croup at her parents' farm at East Kellow. Couch noted that she was 'remarkably insensitive to medicine' despite receiving large doses of antimony and calomel.[7]

Outbreaks of cholera were not infrequent either. The inhabitants of Polperro habitually dumped their sewage into the stream that ran through the middle of the village so that it provided a ready-made waste disposal facility, notwithstanding that it was also used to wash their clothes and that water was drawn from it to wash the fish after it had been gutted. Unsurprisingly, such lack of regard for hygiene inevitably led to recurrent cases of dysentery, typhoid and cholera. Couch recorded an outbreak of dysentery early in 1840 'of not very severe character' but which continued for a long time because those afflicted by it did not regard it as anything particularly serious. In most of the cases he treated, the patient complained of 'cold in the legs' which he concluded 'probably arose from a chill of those parts' after standing on wet ground for long periods.

Couch's concern for the health and general welfare of his patients led him to conclude that the overcrowded living quarters within the small cottages occupied by most families invariably led to the spread of disease and infection. His notes on the 'Health of Dwellings' record that one out of every four children born in England died before the age of five and that damp, airless conditions were the cause of respiratory disease.[8] Tuberculosis, more often referred to as consumption, also claimed the lives of many people during the nineteenth century, particularly among the very young or elderly. Respiratory diseases were ever prevalent, but noticeably more so during prolonged periods of cold and wet weather. An unusually heavy fall of snow in January 1837 followed by a prolonged spell of rain led to an epidemic of bronchial illness, often accompanied by a severe cough and conjunctivitis, the latter caused by riding at night in 'air which is loaded with moisture', Couch concluded.

> 'Towards the end of January this epidemic has very distinctly altered its character, it now attacks with decided vigour a sense of cold, the feet feeling remarkably so, pain and sense of weight along the spinal column at the loins, and severely in the head in some cases and with sickness and loss of appetite. In many instances the pain of the head is local, mostly in one eye and in a few instances this is followed by epitaxis [nose bleed] a smart occasion of fever follows for about two days, rarely exceeding three: then follows profuse perspiration with great soreness in all the limbs even to the tips of the fingers: when the perspiration subsides the debility is very great with severe cough and expectoration but without much mark of inflammation in the chest.'[9]

This outbreak claimed at least one victim, Nicholas Mark, a 40-year-old miller at Crumplehorn; 'a man worn out with disease of the lungs and without proper comforts', according to Couch. He left behind a widow and three young children.

Death was an ever present fact of life in the nineteenth century. In the combined parishes of Talland and Lansallos that comprised most of Couch's patients, an average of 40 burials was recorded each year before 1850, in addition to those lost at sea or elsewhere. And in some years, as in 1820, the death toll rose to over 70. All were sorrowful occasions for the grieving families concerned, none more so than in the case of children and young women.

The sea also claimed the lives of many mariners. The Quillers were not the only Polperro family to lose many of their menfolk at sea and there were other occasions when ships sailing along the coast were driven ashore by storms. In December 1849, the *Shepherdess*, a homeward-bound East Indiaman with a cargo of teak logs, ran on to a reef near Polperro just before midnight and broke in two, spilling her cargo.[10] The captain, his wife and young nephew and all but two of the crew were able to scramble ashore to safety. Couch was called to attend to the captain's wife and the boy following the rescue; a month later he told his son Thomas that 'the labourers at the wreck have ceased their exertions, although much must still remain somewhere hidden, the anchors and cables have been recovered but only one cannon' and, intriguingly, 'none of the marble statues and other curiosities that were on board'.[11] What became of the statues and 'other curiosities' is not known, but much of the teak washed ashore provided valuable building material for the local community.

There were other deaths that had tragic consequences beyond the grave, as in the case of the two Polperro boys who got into a fight in 1853. The younger of the two, ten-year-old Thomas Jasper, died from the effect of two kicks he received in his back from the other, 13-year-old Samuel Good, the son of a local coastguard. The injured boy was confined to bed for eight months before he finally died in December. At the subsequent inquest, Couch testified that death was due to 'concussion of the spinal marrow which would be likely to be produced by a kick'. The jury returned a verdict of manslaughter against Good who was committed for trial at the next assizes in Bodmin.[12]

Then there was the case of poor Elizabeth Turner, a 39-year-old
pauper lunatic and Talland resident who was admitted to the County
Asylum at Bodmin on September 1, 1852.[13] She was very probably still
there when Thomas Quiller Couch, Jonathan Couch's second surgeon
son, found himself temporarily in charge of the asylum soon after
taking up his new post in Bodmin the following year. Polperro would,
of course, have had its share of mentally ill people and those who
would now be described as having learning difficulties. Couch's son
Jonathan was certainly one. But if the poor could not earn a living
because of mental incapacity, or had no one to care for them, they fell
within the new Poor Law. There was nowhere else for them to go but
the asylum at Bodmin.

The Poor Law Act of 1834, which led Charles Dickens to write
Oliver Twist, proved universally unpopular in Cornwall. Conditions
for the rural poor there worsened still further when the potato
crop failed in 1845, ruined by a virulent outbreak of potato blight.
Potatoes and pilchards were the staple diet of many Cornish families
and the famine that followed intensified calls for the repeal of the
Corn Laws, which were designed to support British corn prices against
cheap foreign imports. The blight prompted Couch to send a series
of articles to the Royal Cornwall Polytechnic Society for publication:
*Observations on the Disease which has injured the Potato in the
present year* in 1845, followed two years later by *Further Inquiries
into the Nature and Effects of the prevailing Disease in Potatoes* and
a third the following year.

The cause of potato blight (*Phytophthora infestans*) was not
widely understood at the time, but Couch correctly believed it to be
an airborne disease which he described as a 'poisonous dew'. 'It is
known to cottagers that there are times when, if vegetables covered
with it be gathered at night with the naked hands, inflammation of an
erysipelatous character is the result. This is familiarly termed poisoning
with the dew, and is equally perceptible when the vegetable possesses
no property which can lead us to suppose that any exudation from it
has had any share in producing the effect'.[14]

When the Corn Laws were eventually abolished in 1849 the price
of corn plummeted as cheap imported grain arrived from North
America. Couch was alarmed at the effect this had on farming
in Cornwall as rich farmers retired to live off the interest of their

property while those with smaller farms emigrated to America. 'The price of corn has fallen so low,' he wrote in 1850, 'while the general demands of taxes remain as high as before, that a vast number of estates have been surrendered into the hands of the landlords'.

The crisis directly affected him. He had been compelled to lower the annual rent of his own land at Langreek near Polperro from £70 to £50; 'there was a time when this estate was let for £110' he recorded bitterly in his private memoirs. To make matters worse, he complained, 'the landlord is compelled to pay the tithes, even if, as in such numerous instances, he gets no tenant, and consequently no rent for his estate'. Couch's long held objection to the payment of tithes to the established church was now reinforced by the fact that while 'every landlord has found it necessary to lower his rents ... the Clergy and holders of tithe property have generally and absolutely refused to do so'.[15]

CHAPTER XIII

MAN-MIDWIFE

O ne of the strangest cases encountered by Jonathan Couch during his career as a surgeon-apothecary and man-midwife concerned Mary George, the 32-year-old wife of farm labourer William George. Mary was already the mother of three children and visibly pregnant in June 1840 when she felt the first sensation of the baby's movement in her belly. She was so large that the following month she was unable to continue the sort of work she was accustomed to doing. In November, approaching the time she had been expecting to give birth, she experienced a series of sharp abdominal pains for a day or so. These left her, only to return a fortnight later with even greater severity. Couch, called to examine her, noticed that her arms and legs showed signs of some swelling and that her abdomen was now so distended that she was scarcely able to move.

Mary remained in this condition at her home near Talland until April the following year when she finally went into labour, apparently some 14 months since the start of her pregnancy. Couch attended her again on April 18 when he noted that her cervix was dilated to about three and a half inches in diameter. Some indication of her size can be judged by the fact that he estimated some five gallons of amniotic fluid was discharged when her waters broke. The delivery was further complicated by the fact that the baby was in a transverse position in the womb, necessitating a breech birth. After a period of about an hour and a half, the baby eventually emerged stillborn and evidently malformed. Couch's notes record that it 'had lived close to the period of birth, funis [umbilical chord] short about a foot in length ... the body stout and well formed but the head as if truncated above, the bones apparently loose or rather none, the cavity of the cranium open, spilled with fluid, no neck. The uterus did not contract and a large quantity of liquor amnii was discharged after the birth of the child. The only explanation that can be afforded for this case is that early in pregnancy the uterus became so distended with liquor amnii as to be inadequately contracted, so that when the period of labour approached it was rendered impossible by the circumstance of distension'.[1]

What Couch was describing was a case of anencephaly, resulting in the child being born with a large portion of its brain, skull and scalp missing. But Mary George's prolonged pregnancy seems so extraordinary that it is tempting to dismiss it as improbable. There is certainly no well-documented case of a human pregnancy lasting for 14 months and yet, given the fact that Couch had attended this patient at different stages of her condition, it seems much more likely that Mary herself was mistaken. By the time he assisted at her delivery, he would have attended at several hundred cases of childbirth, many with complications and some even resulting in the death of the mother or child. Deaths in childbirth were always different from all others, however. They were deaths which, in a lifetime of medical practice, Couch never forgot. And the death of a mother, as his own early tragic experience with his first wife had taught him, was not the same as the death of an infant or child.

Infant mortality in the nineteenth century was alarmingly high, particularly in urban areas. Even in south-east Cornwall it accounted for as many as a third of all deaths. Of the 39 recorded burials in 1836 in the combined parishes of Talland and Lansallos, 12 were infants or very young children. Stillbirths were not even recorded, but Couch's medical notebook for that year contains brief details of two cases that he attended. One involved the wife of William Stephens:

> 'It was not easy to ascertain the cause of the child's death,
> but the attending circumstances were these. The mother

was remarkably distended, so as to be able to move but little; and much pain was felt at the sides of the abdomen; and in a lesser degree in front. Her labour was long and somewhat severe, before any dilation of the uterus could be distinguished and when this was considerable and had descended it was with difficulty that the membrane could be ruptured. When there followed a rush of liquor amnii far more abundant than I remember to have met with. The labour afterwards was rather severe, but not long and the child was three times firmly bound round the neck by the cord. The pulse continued for several minutes after birth, but no efforts could produce the action of breathing.'[2]

The following year's entries included the case of Catherine Johns, a 27-year-old farmer's wife at Lanreath who was seven months pregnant with twins when she fell while riding her horse. A week later she went into labour and Couch was present at the delivery of both children, one of which was 'very black on the face and head and though it cried well it died in about three hours; the second child died in about eight hours'. He concluded that the extensive bruising on the one child, coupled with the fact that they were born prematurely, led to their deaths.

Not every birth he attended had such an unhappy outcome, and it is very likely that many women gave birth attended only by a local midwife. Breech births often gave rise to complications however. In the case of one of Couch's neighbours in Polperro, a fisherman's wife in her 30s named Rachel Batten, as many as five out of her first six deliveries were what he termed 'a foot presentation', but at least three of them survived. Another near neighbour and fisherman's wife, Mary Ann Langmaid, was delivered of twin girls by Couch in 1839, one of which was also a 'foot presentation', but happily both survived.

Twins invariably posed problems, as in the case of the boys born to Caroline Brown, a 40-year-old coastguard officer's wife who went into labour at her home in Polperro in December 1840, suffering from oedema and breathing difficulty. 'The first child was moderately stout, the second a fine child, and there was moderate difficulty in its birth yet the funis [umbilical cord] was not sufficiently compressed to have its pulsations stopped: the child remained for nearly half an

hour before breathing was well established but it lived. Neither of
these children cried when born', Couch noted.[3]

Not all his patients were from ordinary working families. One
of the early deliveries he attended, in 1815, was that of Sir Harry
Trelawny's granddaughter, Letitia Harding. Her mother Mary's diary
for September 4 records that she felt 'very unwell the whole day...
after tea I felt the tears in my eyes at the thoughts of what I should
perhaps go thro'... About 8 or 9 sent for Mr Couch'. The entry for the
following day begins: 'Early in the morning was born a little girl after
a dismal long labour'.[4]

Couch's medical notebooks record only those cases that he deemed
noteworthy. Nevertheless, of the 30 or so cases that he recorded in a
five year period between 1836 and 1841, no fewer than 16 involved
childbirth complications of one sort or another. Many involved
intensely difficult intra-uterine manoeuvres carried out in distant
houses and cottages with no possibility of outside assistance, stretching
his skills to the very limit. His life-long concern about premature
birth and abortions is well illustrated by the case of Maria Job, whose
husband Ananiah was a cousin of Zephaniah Job, the 'smugglers'
banker'.

Maria had already given birth to three healthy children but, in
November 1837, she aborted a male foetus at four months. Couch
noted that the aborted baby had a twisted foot and a soft tumour
on the top of its head where part of the skull was missing and it
was this, he believed, that caused the rejection of the foetus. 'I
am convinced that a very large proportion of abortions proceed
from leaving off the foetus because it is incapable of proceeding
in natural development,' he wrote. 'The action of quickening is not
merely the first act of muscular exertion, but it is a very important
process in which animal life begins; the nervous or cerebral action
then come increasing and shooting its energy through the system.
When the faulty organization does not admit of this the embryo
must die.'[5]

There is no doubt that man-midwifery as it became known
occupied a considerable part of the routine practice of a country
surgeon-apothecary like Couch. It was an exhausting part of any
doctor's work in the early half of the nineteenth century, often
demanding judgement, skill and quick-thinking. 'Deliver the babies

and you will have the family as patients for the rest of your life' was the received wisdom of the day.[6] But many medical practitioners of the period regarded it as time-consuming and poorly paid in terms of the time and energy it demanded.

Some measure of the satisfaction that Couch himself derived from bringing children into the world can be gleaned from an entry in his personal memoirs on September 5, 1861: 'I suppose I am able to say what no other medical practitioner in the county can say, perhaps no other in the kingdom. I have this day attended the birth of a child, which is the sixth generation I have known familiarly, both of the father's side, and the mother's: and four of these generations I have attended in child birth'.[7]

The child in question was Robert Hicks whose father and grandfather, also called Robert; great-grandmother Ann Willcock and her father and grandfather, both named John, had all been patients of Couch during the 50 years he had been in practice in Polperro. And because the fishing families had a long tradition of inter-marrying, the same could be said for the maternal side of Robert Hicks's family as well. It was indeed a remarkable claim for any doctor to be able to make, and very probably justified. Many of his patients were far from wealthy and his fees for treatment were invariably small; in some cases he attended whole families for years without receiving, or expecting, a penny. And if an elderly patient called on him to ask for 'a bottle o' trade for the stomach', more often than not he would hand them a shilling with the words, 'Here! A beef steak will do you more good than my physic,' and return to his writing again.[8]

Early on, Couch learned how some of his poorer patients would resort to popular cures handed down through the generations, many based on old superstitions. Among farming communities, children afflicted with whooping cough were often taken to a piebald horse and passed three times under its belly in the firm belief that a cure would result. Boils were thought to be cured by creeping on hands and knees beneath a bramble which had grown into the soil at both ends. And the cures for warts were many and various. Such superstitions abounded among Cornish folk but Couch was careful to point out that 'though superstitious, they are, with regard to the realities of life, as shrewd and sagacious as their neighbours'.[9]

CHAPTER XIV

A GOOD HORSE

Two things above all were essential for success as a country doctor in the nineteenth century: a good reputation and a good horse.[1] Couch undoubtedly possessed the former and there is plenty of evidence that he had the latter as well. He would certainly have been entirely dependent on his horse when visiting patients away from Polperro itself for the terrain in that part of Cornwall consists largely of hills and steep-sided valleys. Travel on horseback was the preferred method of transport for country medical practitioners at the time; for them a horse became their faithful servant and constant companion. The sight of the Polperro doctor trotting round the country lanes in all weathers was a familiar one; as were tales of his cob seen patiently tethered to a gate at dawn while its rider pursued a rare luminous moth or some other elusive insect in the field beyond. In his later years Couch used a gig, and often gentry or farmers at a distance would send out their own gigs or carriages for him.[2]

Travel by horseback at least provided the doctor with unexpected opportunities to observe the natural world around him. Riding home in a particularly violent thunderstorm one summer's evening in 1832, for example, Couch had a narrow escape when he witnessed a ball of light about the size of an orange shoot across his path at head height about 20 yards in front of him 'as if projected from a cannon ... The whole was the work of an instant; the ball, of a steel blue

... unattended by any noise or explosion and evidently unconnected with the lightning that glared around'.[3] And as usual, his keen powers of observation resulted in yet another contribution to one of those scientific journals so popular with Victorian readers, the *Magazine of Natural History*, this time on *Luminous Meteors commonly called Shooting Stars*.

Times were changing fast, however, and the old route that led into Polperro from the east down Talland Hill was too steep; it was difficult even for riders on horseback, let alone horse drawn carts or carriages. Couch's daughter, Bertha, described it as 'a road so steep and rocky, that to scramble up or down it seems a more fitting expression than to walk, ride or drive'.[4] Plans for a new road to follow a different line down the coomb through the hamlet of Crumplehorn had been proposed by a local engineer and planner named Joseph Thomas. Consent was obtained from Nicholas Kendall of Killigarth Manor on whose land the road would pass, and in December 1848 the far-sighted Couch presided at a public meeting in the Ship Inn to discuss the project. Improvements had already been made to the ancient road that led from Torpoint and the Cremyl Passage ferry to Liskeard, with parts of the route rebuilt to avoid hills and ensure the swifter passage of the mail coaches. Work on the new road from Torpoint to Looe had also begun and Couch realised that Polperro was in danger of being left still cut off from the outside world by land, with almost everything coming in and out by sea. As a result of his initiative, the money for the new road into Polperro was raised by private subscription, with everyone contributing something, however small.

Work began at last in February the following year. Couch recorded in his notebook: 'At 4 o'clock in the afternoon of a very fine day, a commencement was made, by my laying the first stone of a new bridge at Crumplehorn, to be called Kendall Bridge. I deposited there several copper coins of our Sovereign and others, amidst the hearty cheers of several hundred spectators, with numerous flags flying.'[5]

The New Road, as it became known, followed the line of a narrow farm track that had led up from Crumplehorn Mill to Mortha Gate at the top, a distance of just over half a mile, and was finally opened with much pomp and ceremony on Wednesday, July 11, 1849. It was a fine summer's day and shortly after two o'clock in the afternoon a procession of nearly one thousand men, women and children set off from Polperro up Talland Hill, headed by the Polperro band and a decorated boat on wheels pulled by a team of fishermen. At the junction with the new road at the top of the hill a gate was opened and the procession continued down the new road to Crumplehorn where tea was served while the band played. 'The whole town of Polperro also was ornamented with numerous triumphal arches formed of trees and branches, with flags and a strong rope was stretched from Hard Head across the top of Hobb's Hill decorated with a variety of flags,' noted Couch who later wrote of the new road: 'It is one of the greatest improvements which the town has seen within living memory'.[6]

The benefit was immediately apparent. Horse-drawn vehicles of all sizes were now able to enter Polperro and it was not long before a regular horse-bus service operated as far as Plymouth, where the railway line to London had recently opened. The only alternative to the carriers with their horse-drawn vans toiling their way up the hills was the sea, by the coastal vessels plying their way between the two ports. Plans were already being drawn up for a new bridge to replace the narrow one that existed between East and West Looe and Couch was among those invited to attend the ceremonial laying of the first stone in the summer of 1854. The scene, as recalled by him, was reminiscent of the opening of the New Road at Polperro:

'I found both towns gaily dressed out with triumphal arches and flags, an arch of verdure at each end of the Bridge, at various distances along the chief streets at East Looe, and near the Town Hall of that Borough were numerous trees fixed in the ground, so as to look like a grove. All the vessels in the harbour were dressed in flags, and a rope was drawn across the river, from the higher road passing from the Bridge to West Looe, across to the top mast of a brig on the East Looe side, which line was dressed in a variety of colours. The procession was formed of numerous gentlemen, who assembled at the Town Hall: and who, with a band from Menheniot, marched through the streets, over the Bridge, to West Looe, round the new built Market house there and then back to the place where the foundation stone was to be laid, and where a party of ladies had assembled.'[7]

The ceremony was performed by John Francis Buller of Morval who had contributed £300 towards the cost of the project, and in time-honoured tradition, a set of copper coins of Queen Victoria were laid at the foundation.' Couch, who had also been consulted by the Clerk of Works about the suitability of the stone at Barcelona quarry near Trelawne used for the new bridge, attended the official opening in Looe in September the following year.[8]

Couch rarely travelled far from his neighbourhood in Cornwall but as his fame spread in the scientific world many people came to Polperro to consult him. Letters arrived from all parts of the world, some merely addressed to Couch, Jonathan Esq., Cornwall. Among his visitors was the future Poet Laureate, Alfred Tennyson.

Tennyson had arrived in Fowey in June 1848 to gather material for his *Idylls of the King*, a series of narrative poems that retold the legend of King Arthur. Couch went to see him in Fowey and the following day Tennyson came by boat to Polperro for tea with the doctor, accompanied by a coastguard officer and amateur naturalist named Charles Peach already known to Couch. It was an auspicious occasion but Couch was not altogether impressed with Tennyson's appearance: 'I find him well informed, and communicative; I believe a good Greek scholar, with some knowledge of Hebrew. His personal appearance is not prepossessing: having a slouch in his gait, and rather slovenly in his dress, though his clothes were new and good. He confesses to this. He admired the wildness of our scenery, and deprecated the breaking in of improvements, as they are termed. He enquired after traditions, especially of the great Arthur, his object in visiting the County being, to collect materials for a poem on that chief. But he almost doubted his existence.'[9]

Poet and village doctor had one thing in common. Both were meticulous in their research before publishing. Tennyson always tried to visit the scene of any poem he composed to absorb the scenery: 'Sometimes I want to compose a stanza or two and to find a quiet nook where I can wind off my words...'[10]

Two years before Tennyson's arrival in Fowey, Couch had been there with other members of his family to see the young Queen Victoria arrive aboard the royal yacht with Prince Albert on September 8, 1846. The royal couple came ashore at the quay that has since been named after Albert, passing within a yard of Couch as he stood in the crowd

25

Jonathan Couch near the foot of the New Road into Polperro
above Crumplehorn Mill. He is wearing his top hat, frock coat,
pebble spectacles and carrying a large rolled umbrella.

26

The landing of a thrasher shark in Polperro in 1865. The man on the right
is directing a villager to collect water, to pour over the shark to help keep its
natural colour for Couch to see.

27

A full length portrait of Jonathan Couch
by Lewis Harding.

28

Sarah Lander (née Roose), Jonathan's third wife.
They were married in 1858 when he was 68 and she was 21.
(*Royal Institution of Cornwall*)

29

Sarah (1862-1945) and Bertha (1860-1940) Couch,
elder daughters of Jonathan and Sarah.
(*Royal Institution of Cornwall*)

30

A rare photograph of Jonathan Couch with his daughter Bertha.
(*Royal Institution of Cornwall*)

31

The postage stamp featuring Couch's drawing of a short-spined
sea-scorpion issued by the Post Office in January 1988 to mark the
bicentenary of the Linnean Society.

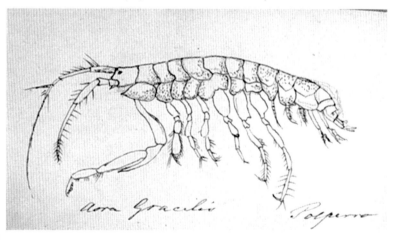

32

First entry in one of Couch's many notebooks, dated 1853.
(*Royal Institution of Cornwall*)

33

Couch's drawing of a sandhopper (*Aora Gracilis*) originally identified
by Charles Spence Bate, a year before the discovery of a similar species
near Polperro in 1858 and named *Philoscia couchii*.
(*Royal Institution of Cornwall*)

Jonathan Couch, Surgeon Apothercary of Polperro
(*Photograph by Lewis Harding c1865*)

35

Obelisk erected in the cemetery at Mabel Barrow at Lansallos
in memory of Jonathan Couch and his second wife, Jane.

36

The white marble memorial tablet (below) unveiled
in the Methodist church in Polperro in 1929.

that had gathered to greet them while Jane, his wife, watched from a shop window just behind. Victoria, aged 27 at the time and in only the 10th year of her reign, travelled in the royal carriage to the Trinity iron mine near Lostwithiel where she was presented with samples of ore, described by Couch as 'some not very remarkable pieces of iron ore contained in a common wooden handled box' as well as a miner's helmet 'worthy of a place in a Royal, tho' not scientific, collection'. Even if he was not impressed, the Queen evidently was for she commanded that 50 gold sovereigns be distributed among the miners.

Writing to his son Richard in Penzance, Couch said: 'The people were exceedingly pleased at the Queen's walking thro' the streets: but I believe the cause to have been her dislike, or even fear to be driven thro' Fowey streets which assuredly were not formed to receive wheeled carriages – thus it seems we can even match Penzance in a Royal visit'.[11] Ten years later Prince Albert sent him a copy of *The Natural History of Dee Side and Braemar* edited by Dr. Edwin Lankester. Couch was naturally flattered, though unsure quite what he had done to merit it: 'Perhaps a present accepted by his Royal Highness of my Cornish Fauna has something to do with it,' he wondered.[12]

In the first decade of Queen Victoria's reign coastal steam-packets operated regularly between Plymouth and Falmouth and Couch occasionally used the service to travel to west Cornwall. Though faster and more reliable than sailing vessels, the packets were nevertheless susceptible to the weather. On a visit to Truro in the summer of 1839, he wrote to his wife Jane to let her know that he would be returning to Liskeard by coach rather than by the *Sir Francis Drake* packet because of the 'chance of a rough sea, and perhaps not being taken out by a Boat', adding 'if you will send a horse (to be left at the Union Inn) I hope to be home in good time on Wednesday'.[13]

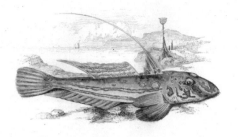

CHAPTER XV

'HORRID OLD MAN'

When his second wife Jane died in September 1857, followed four months later by their only daughter Margaret, Couch was left at home in Polperro with his mentally impaired son Jonathan, aged 38, and his youngest son, John, assisting his father with his medical practice.

Margaret, 40 and unmarried, had been in poor health for many years. She was buried alongside her mother at the little Wesleyan graveyard at Mabel Barrow that Couch had created following the Lansallos rector's refusal to bury his granddaughter ten years earlier. Of Margaret, he wrote, 'What a contrast has her life been, and now her death, to the anticipations formed at her birth! A sweet babe, her mother's only daughter, she was much loved, but convulsions at a very early age, ruined her nervous system'.[1]

His daughter's death, coming so soon after her mother's, plunged Couch into a period of depression, further aggravated by an attack of bronchitis in February the following year. In a revealing private memoranda to his son Thomas, he wrote that he had been ill for more than ten days with a chest infection and 'harassing coughs' but had nevertheless had to both prepare medicine for himself and even occasionally visit his more seriously ill patients despite being in some considerable pain himself. He complained of being neglected by his daughter Jane Hitchens, her aunt Elizabeth Lane and other members of his family. 'From the first day of my illness no one at anytime ever passed five minutes at one time in my bedroom ... I record those particulars as an example of what I am to meet with in case of future sickness & still more of old age.'[2]

It was an uncharacteristic display of self-pity but short-lived. For a while, he remained at home scarcely seeing anyone, and attending only the most urgent medical cases. He even gave serious consideration to giving up his practice and devoting the rest of his life to his scientific work. But a chance encounter with the mother of one of his patients led to a dramatic change of heart.

The mother in question was Mrs Eliza Roose, the wife an elderly local coastguard named Robert, whose 21-year-old daughter Sarah had been treated by Couch for what he diagnosed as 'brain fever' but was more likely viral meningitis. Sarah had been engaged to a young man named Samuel Langmaid two years earlier who caught a severe chill in the New Year of 1856 after travelling from Polperro to Plymouth in the horse-bus that operated twice a week. As there was not enough room for him to travel inside the bus, he was obliged to ride outside. The weather that day was cold and wet and, by the time he arrived at Plymouth several hours later, Samuel was chilled to the bone and soaked to the skin. Within days, he was taken ill and for four or five weeks lay in his lodgings visited by family and friends, including Sarah Roose. When he failed to respond to treatment, his doctor advised him to return to Polperro and he duly arrived there late one evening in a very weak and exhausted state.

So concerned was she at the condition of her fiancé that Sarah went at once to the Polperro doctor and asked him to come and see Samuel immediately. Unluckily for her, Couch made no secret of the fact that he did not like be called out at night except for the most urgent cases. All too often he had been called on late in the evening to attend to a patient who had been ill all day and had waited until bedtime to send for him. Now in his mid 60s, he was even less inclined to be roused after dark, especially if he had settled down among his books and papers. Sarah's pleas for him to attend to Samuel were met with such indignant displeasure that she went back to friends and told them, 'Never send for that horrid old man'.

But not even Couch's skill could save young Samuel Langmaid and the chill rapidly developed into tuberculosis. Within a few weeks he was dead and Sarah was plunged into inconsolable grief.

Two year later, she too was lying seriously ill at her home in Talland Street, now attended by the 'horrid old man'. Her recovery was painfully slow and Couch soon became aware that she was unlikely ever to get better in her present state of mind, tormented by grief and depression. He discussed her condition with her on several occasions and eventually realised that she was still feeling bitterly aggrieved at his gruff response the night she had called on him to attend her fiancé. Troubled, he sat at home in his study brooding over what he could do to aid Sarah's recovery. She was, after all, an intelligent and spirited young woman who would make an ideal companion and wife for any man; having recently lost his own dear wife and daughter, he was aware of a growing feeling of tenderness towards her. And, after giving the matter some considerable thought, he came to the extraordinary conclusion that the best treatment he could offer her was marriage.

Understandably, in view of the difference in their ages, Couch was very doubtful that such an attractive young woman would even accept such a proposal from an old man in his 70th year. But, with nothing to lose but his pride, the doctor wrote off to a firm of jewellers in Plymouth and ordered an engagement brooch. When it arrived, he called at the coastguard's home and presented the brooch to Sarah, telling her she was not to accept it unless her answer to his proposal of marriage was 'Yes'. Her immediate response was, 'Why, Mr Couch, you are an old man!' but on being urged to give the matter careful consideration, she did so and in due course consented to become his wife.[3]

News of the doctor's engagement to Sarah astonished almost everyone because of the disparity of their ages, and there was a buzz of excited gossip throughout the whole neighbourhood. Many people were pleased for him, but there were those who disapproved of the match and expressed surprise that he should choose such a young and inexperienced girl for a wife, while others thought he should have chosen someone nearer his own age as a housekeeper. The Roose family did not wholly approve of the marriage, neither did Couch's eldest son Richard, but Thomas at least was delighted that his father would have someone to care for him in his old age. In any event, the engagement certainly provoked plenty of gossip, providing a talking point for months.

A cryptic page in Couch's own private memoirs gives some indication of his determination not to yield to pressure from family and others to break off the engagement. Written largely in a personal code of nouns, phrases, abbreviations and Latin that clearly relate to his intention to marry his much younger fiancée, the words 'passion', 'abuse', 'demand' and 'delinquency' can be made out together with a final defiant 'I shan't break it off'. His mind was made up. No amount of disapprobation was going to change it.[4]

The couple were married quietly at the Green Bank Chapel in Liskeard on October 23, 1858, accompanied by Sarah's 34-year-old step-sister Elizabeth. Couch attended to the process of obtaining a marriage licence, thus avoiding the need to have the banns read at either Talland or Lansallos parish churches, and the ceremony was conducted by the Reverend Charles Edwards of the United Methodist Free Church (previously known as the Wesleyan Methodist Association).

In September 1860 Sarah gave birth to a daughter, Bertha, attended by her husband. A second daughter, Sarah, followed in 1862 but a third, Lydia, born in November 1863 with a hare lip among other complications, did not survive more than a few days.[5]

The septuagenarian Couch still derived great pleasure from his new young family. Sir John Salusbury Trelawny, who had inherited the baronetcy from his grandfather Sir Harry, called on the doctor at his home one day in 1865 to find him repeating 'Who killed Cock Robin?' to his two-year-old daughter Sarah. Sir John, much amused by what he saw, said, 'Well, I can understand it, doctor; my grandchildren seem more to me than my own did, and I fancy these little ones come to you much in the same light'. At the time, Couch had just completed a little book entitled *Vindication of the probability of the Story of Brut, and the Existence of Giants in Cornwall and Devon*, which lay on the table of his study, ready for posting to his publisher. On another occasion, Bertha Couch recalled her father returning home with two tiny irons for her doll's clothes, having taken particular care in selecting them at the shop where they were purchased.[6]

His enthusiasm for observing the natural world was equally undiminished. At home with his little daughters, Couch spent many days studying the activity of a common garden spider that had established itself in the corner of the porch at the entrance to their house. No one was allowed to disturb the creature; patients were directed to use the rear entrance while Couch himself would often call his wife to come and watch as the spider captured prey ensnared in its web then quickly wrapped it in silk before devouring it. He marvelled at the way it would clean and repair its web each day, removing the dust, dirt and dew that accumulated overnight. 'That little gentleman has more sense in his head than half our tradesmen,' he was memorably heard to say.[7] Couch's observations naturally led to his submitting an article to the *Intellectual Observer: A Review of Natural History, Microscopic Research, and Recreative Science*, a forerunner of what is now the journal *Nature*.

The young Mrs Couch was expecting a fourth child the following year and in June 1867 duly gave birth to yet another daughter, Clarinda. Couch, now 78 years of age, was busy preparing a paper on the results of the dredging operations along the Cornish coast to be read at a meeting of the Royal Cornwall Polytechnic Society in Falmouth. At the same time, he dispatched a specimen of a rare sucking fish that had been sent to him from Mevagissey and another of a spider crab to the Cornwall Museum at Truro.

In September the following year he received a visit from Frank Buckland, the editor of a scientific periodical called *Land and Water* to which Couch had occasionally contributed articles. Buckland was accompanied by Abraham Bartlett of the Zoological Society of London in Regent's Park, widely regarded as one of the greatest of all zoological garden superintendents and famed for his displays of taxidermy at the Great Exhibition in 1851. The three men discussed the latest techniques for preserving and mounting fish, one of the most difficult branches of taxidermy, a popular art form pioneered by Victorians. Creating a technically accurate fish mount remained one of the greatest challenges and the best results were only achieved by some of the outstanding artists of their day. Couch's knowledge and skill - developed over years of producing remarkably accurate and lifelike coloured drawings of fish specimens - was eagerly sought and freely given.

Couch's interests were not confined solely to matters of natural history. The return of a Liberal government headed by William Gladstone in 1868 directed attention to Ireland where there had been growing unrest ever since the potato famine. Gladstone's attempt to placate the Irish by disestablishing the Church of Ireland prompted Couch to write to the prime minister suggesting that any surplus funds that arose from such a policy should be used to reduce the national debt.[8]

CHAPTER XVI

MYSTERIOUS FOSSILS

From early childhood, Jonathan Couch had explored almost every accessible part of the shore between Looe and the Fowey estuary, searching tidal rock pools and delving into crevices in search of flora and fauna of any kind he could find. It was a passion that his eldest son Richard inherited and shared.

Returning to Polperro in 1838 to work with his father after qualifying, Richard, in whatever time could be spared from his father's patients, would set off along the coastal path in either direction from Polperro in pursuit of his particular study of zoophytes. These curious creatures inhabit the shoreline in huge numbers but invariably pass unnoticed to casual observers: sea anemones, corals, sponges and a host of other invertebrate animals that look more like plants. Day after day, the 22-year-old doctor would return home carrying a variety of specimens gathered during his explorations; these would then be carefully examined under a microscope, drawings made and each one meticulously recorded and written up. Couch himself, of course, took a keen interest in his son's findings, believing that the very simplicity of such primitive sea animals could lead to a greater understanding of more complex creatures.

By 1841 Richard had amassed enough material to publish a paper entitled *A Natural History of Cornish Zoophytes* which he

presented to the Royal Cornwall Polytechnic Society in Penzance that
year. So impressed were the members, among whom were some of
the most distinguished Cornishmen of their day, that they awarded
him the Society's Silver Medal. The following year he added a second
paper, *Observations on the Sponges of Cornwall* as well as another,
Observations on the Development of the Frog. Further recognition of
his scientific studies came when a new species of sea anemone he had
discovered on one of his sea shore excursions was named after him.
Zoanthus couchii was the name given to the specimen he submitted
to Dr George Johnston, one of the most eminent naturalists in Britain
at the time.

Richard was now a member of the Polytechnic Society's committee
and his father was soon to be appointed a Vice-President. The annual
report of 1843 noted 'two original communications of great value, on
the Crustaceans, were received from the Messrs. Couch of Polperro,
many of whose communications have previously added to the value
of the society's reports'. Father and son were making their mark.

When Richard eventually published his work on Cornish
zoophytes, it not only contained much new information on the
habits of these little known creatures but added several new
species to the list of those already known to exist in the British
Isles. In a preface, he wrote: 'The Zoophytes at present existing
on our shores are small and fragile when compared with those
of warmer climates; yet the limestone of Devon and the slate
rocks of Cornwall contain the remains of specimens, which for
size and beauty might have vied with any now existing. Though
the Cornish species are small, yet many of them are exceedingly
elegant and seem peculiarly fitted to invite attention. To myself the
investigation has been rather the amusement of leisure hours and
pleasurable excursions on the water, than a study; had it however
been otherwise the pleasure derived from it would be more than
compensated for any difficulties that could have occurred'.[1]

Richard moved to Penzance in March 1844 where he planned to
set up a practice despite knowing very few people there. When he left
the family home in Polperro, his father wished him well in his career
among the mining communities of west Cornwall though saddened,
no doubt, to be parted from the son with whom he shared so much
knowledge of the natural world.

A few years earlier, Richard had come across a strange-looking mollusc in West Coomb in Lantivet Bay, just below Lansallos church two miles to the west of Polperro. At the time, neither father nor son had been able to identify it. On a visit to his family during the summer of 1851, however, Richard obtained some further specimens which his father sent off to Joshua Alder in Newcastle, whose study of British molluscs had recently been published. Although the specimens had died by the time they reached their destination, Alder was able to identify them as a rare sort of sea slug, *Onchidium celticum*, originally discovered by a French naturalist earlier in the nineteenth century.[2]

Couch obtained several more specimens from the spot in Lantivet Bay where Richard had first found the mollusc and succeeded in sending them, still alive, to Alder in Newcastle. He also informed the Linnean Society of the find. Word of the creature's discovery on the shores of Britain spread quickly among the scientific world and Couch eventually received a request from John Edward Gray at the British Museum for some specimens to be added to the museum's collection. He was at pains to point out, however, that it was his son Richard who had made the original discovery and not himself: 'He therefore is the real discoverer of this creature in Britain'.[3]

In the summer of 1851, as millions flocked to the Great Exhibition in London's Hyde Park, two leading scientists of the day headed instead to Cornwall in search of fossils. One of them, Professor Adam Sedgwick, had greatly influenced Charles Darwin's early studies and was regarded as one of the founders of modern geology. His travelling companion was the equally learned Professor Frederick McCoy, an Irish born physician and keeper of the Woodwardian Museum at Cambridge University. One of their objectives was a meeting with the Polperro doctor whose discovery of some mysterious fossils nearly ten years earlier had aroused much curiosity and controversy in the scientific world since the received wisdom of the day was that no fossil remains were likely to be found in Cornwall.

Couch was delighted to receive such distinguished visitors and readily gave them some samples of the fossils he had found among the 400 million years old Lower Devonian slate beds below the cliffs that extended either side of Polperro. The three men went to examine the spot where Couch had originally found them while climbing up over some steep rocks below Chapel cliff on the west side of the harbour.

When Couch had first discovered the fossils in 1842 he had been puzzled by what he had found, but eventually decided they were coral, a view that was shared by several other geologists whom he contacted. But word of the find soon reached Charles Peach, the coastguard officer who had accompanied Tennyson during the Poet Laureate's visit to Couch in Polperro five years earlier. He had become known to Couch while stationed further along the coast at Gorran Haven several years earlier and their acquaintance grew out of a shared interest in fossils and marine fauna. Peach wasted no time in visiting the spot and collecting further specimens which, he decided, were the remains of cuttlefish. It was not long before he brought his 'find' to the attention of the British Association for the Advancement of Science at its annual meeting held in Cork in 1843, causing quite a stir in the process.

Couch's understandable annoyance at Peach's claim to have discovered the fossils himself was compounded by the fact that they were described as fish remains. Known as the 'Cornish Ichthyolites', they quickly became a controversial topic in scientific circles, with several eminent geologists agreeing with Peach, including William Pengelly, the geologist and archaeologist best remembered for his exploration of Kent's Hole cavern near Torquay. Pengelly did at least credit Jonathan and Richard Couch with having been the first people to have found them.

Still holding to his view that they were the remains of coral, Couch was surprised to hear Professors Sedgwick and McCoy say they shared his belief that the fossils were not the remains of fish, although they were uncertain as to exactly what they might be.[4] A few months later he was to learn that McCoy, who shared Couch's passion for natural history, had published an account of the Polperro fossils in which he identified them as a very rare species of sponge named *Steganodictyum*. 'These curious zoophytes abound in a particular layer of dark Devonian schist near Polperro on the coast of Cornwall'.

Further support for his view came from the acclaimed Scottish geologist, Hugh Miller, who delivered a paper on what had now become known as the 'Polperro Fossils' to the Royal Physical Society in Edinburgh in which he said they were the most puzzling things he had ever seen – 'riddles on which to exercise the ingenuity of the Paleontologist'.[5]

It was not the end of the matter however. In 1865 yet another distinguished surgeon and naturalist, Dr. Edwin Lankester, came to the conclusion that the Polperro fossils were indeed the remains of a species of scaly primitive fish that probably inhabited river estuaries along the Cornish coast millions of years ago. Lankester, as President of the British Association, had been present at the famous debate in 1860 when the Bishop of Oxford, Samuel Wilberforce, attempted to pour scorn on Darwin's *Origin of Species* by asking Thomas Henry Huxley 'was it through his grandfather or his grandmother that he claimed his descent from a monkey?' Huxley memorably retorted that he 'was not ashamed to have a monkey for his ancestor, but he would be ashamed to be connected with a man who used great gifts to obscure the truth'.

The debate over the 'Polperro Fossils' that continued among leading geologists and palaeontologists throughout Britain was further fuelled by yet another fossil discovery in south Cornwall in 1854, this time in the quarry near Trelawne where stone was being extracted for the building of the new road bridge in Looe. Couch sent off several samples to the Royal Geological Society of Cornwall with the following comment: 'Hitherto no fish has been discovered to have left its remains embedded in our rocks; and therefore it is not without considerable hesitation that I venture to introduce to the Society what appears to me to belong to this order of vertebrated animals... This fossil, if a fish, belongs to the Order Pleuronectidae or flat fishes'.[6]

So, if the fossils in the quarry at Trelawne were the remains of a flat fish, were the earlier finds under the cliffs along the coast below also those of fish? Couch still stuck to his belief that the earlier finds were sponges, but it was William Pengelly who finally settled the matter when, some 25 years after the initial discovery of the so-called 'Polperro Fossils', he declared them all to have been identified as a long extinct genus of fish, *Pteraspis* – 'they are all fragments of fish, not sponge'.

Charles Peach, who had contradicted Couch's original opinion of the Polperro fossil remains, was eventually transferred from Fowey to a position at Peterhead in Scotland at the end of 1849, but not before he was honoured with medals from the Royal Cornwall Polytechnic Society for his geological discoveries and had sold the remains of his fossil collection to the Royal Cornwall Geological Society for £20, having already presented a selection of them to Prince Albert. This prompted Couch to comment: 'Peach was always eager to get the price of what he could obtain, and all his efforts were under the bias of a wish for promotion, all of which was in a degree excusable, because he had a numerous family entirely dependent on him'.

Indeed, Peach became known in some circles as the Cornish Geologist, an appellation that must have irked Couch, and had already been exalted in Chambers's *Edinburgh Journal*, a forerunner of the famous encyclopaedia:

> 'But who is that little intelligent-looking man in a faded naval uniform, who is so invariably to be seen in a particular central seat in this section? That, gentle reader, is perhaps one of the most interesting men who attend the British Association. He is only a private in the mounted guard (preventive service) at an obscure part of the Cornwall coast, with four shillings a day, and a wife and nine children, most of whose education he has himself to conduct. He never tastes the luxuries which are so common in the middle ranks of life, and even amongst a large portion of the working classes. He has to mend with his own hands every sort of thing that can break or wear in his house. Yet Mr. Peach is a votary of Natural History; not a student of the science in books, for he cannot afford books; but an investigator by sea and shore, a collector of Zoophytes and Echinodermata - strange creatures, many of which are as yet hardly known to man. These he collects, preserves, and describes; and every year does he come up to the British Association with a few novelties of this kind, accompanied by illustrative papers and drawings.'

Despite this, Couch was typically generous about Peach, saying he believed him to be 'a warm hearted and honest man, with a good degree of vanity,' but added pointedly, 'in regard to science, not capable of writing a book on any subject although he could materially assist one who could do so'.[7]

'My impressions of Peach as a geologist,' Couch wrote later, 'are that industrious zeal was his chief characteristic, for his knowledge was neither extensive nor accurate, and however positive he might be in regard his names, they cannot by any means be depended on. He said and wrote all he knew; and it may be said without injustice, some times more. On other departments of science he was still more deficient in knowledge, but his eagerness to secure whatever was new or interesting could not fail to lead to some interesting results. From his eagerness also to spread the knowledge of what he knew or found of Cornish geology, he was led to mention things which caused the impression that he was the discoverer of them. Such, for instance, as the discovery of what are termed the fish beds at Polperro: but in fact they were discovered by myself: it is true I did not believe them to be remains of fishes, but of corals, and such I think them still, but when Peach supposed them fishes, he meant the bones of cuttlefishes, though this was changed afterwards.'[8]

It was probably not the only time an ambitious amateur geologist claimed credit for the findings of another and Couch very likely went to his grave still believing that the fossils he had found were the remains of coral. Even today the specimens on display at the Royal Cornwall Museum in Truro credit Peach as having been the first to discover them.

As word of Couch's discoveries along his native shoreline spread, other marine zoologists travelled to Cornwall in search of specimens and perhaps an opportunity of meeting the doctor himself. Among them was Charles Spence Bate, a dentist who had devoted his life to the study of marine biology and became a regular correspondent with Charles Darwin following publication of the latter's *Journal of researches into the Geology and Natural History of the Various Countries visited by H.M.S. Beagle* in 1839. Bate had moved to Plymouth where he helped set up the Marine Biological Association in 1884 and became an acknowledged authority on crustaceans.

In 1858 he paid a visit to Couch in the company of Professor John Robert Kinahan, an Irish physician who had written several books on crab larvae. As the three men were returning to Polperro along the cliff path in Talland Bay at high tide, they paused to spend time examining whatever they could find among the sand and seaweed above the high water mark. There, among large numbers of several species of woodlice already known to them, they were amazed to discover one particular specimen that differed from those already identified and catalogued. A new species perhaps? Samples were taken by Professor Kinahan who later informed Couch that it was indeed a new species.[9]

Couch's reward came nine years later when he received a copy of Charles Spence Bate's latest book on *British Sessile-eyed Crustacea*. Turning to page 452, he was delighted to read a description of the unusual-looking woodlouse they found in Talland Bay under the name of *Philoscia couchii*. Professor Kinahan, who had identified it as an entirely new species, added the comment: 'I have named Philoscia Couchii in memorial of one of the pioneers in the study of the zoological geography of England, and of a few pleasant hours spent in his company'. It was an honour that marked the high esteem in which the Polperro doctor was held by the scientific community of the day.[10]

In the summer of 1866, a series of dredging excursions were carried out off the south east coast of Cornwall under the supervision of Charles Spence Bate, funded by the British Association for the Advancement of Science. The dredge used would have been similar to the trawl net employed by Cornish fishermen at the time and sweeps of the sea bed were carried out at depths varying from 180 feet to 300 feet some 20 miles out to sea. Couch's role aboard the vessel was the careful inspection of the net each time it was hauled aboard, collecting items he thought worthy of further study and identification.

As luck would have it, the weather that summer was particularly wet and windy (even the Fowey regatta was disrupted by a south-westerly gale in August), making conditions on board the dredging vessel unpleasant even for the crew let alone the passengers. Couch had enlisted the help of several local fishermen and also of William Laughrin, a Polperro coastguard who lived along the Warren and had demonstrated a keen interest in natural history, having assisted Couch on a number of occasions in gathering specimens of fish and other marine animals. Large numbers of crabs and other shellfish, as well as jellyfish, sponges, marine worms and starfish were brought up in the net for the doctor to examine. On one occasion, when the trawl net was hauled on board it was found to include a large jellyfish inside of which was concealed a total of 62 young scads (horse mackerel). This astonishing find led Couch to speculate whether, since the jellyfish found off Cornwall invariably came from warmer waters further south, they might be the carriers of other rarer species of fish not usually found off the shores of Britain.[11]

If the dredging exercises provided many hours of absorbing pleasure for Couch, they rapidly became a trial for his wife Sarah at home in Polperro with their two young daughters. After each trip, specimens were brought to the doctor's house where they were examined, classified, commented on, and preserved. Bertha, their eldest daughter, recalled later that 'soon the air was permeated with the smell of fish and the constant in-and-out of men in sea-boots who, disregarding doormats, left scraps of seaweed or fish scales on the carpets, made the time a season of irritability of temper rather than pleasure in scientific research'.[12]

In due course, many of the specimens from the dredging were sent to various museums, including the British Museum where John Edward Gray took a particular interest in Couch's findings. Among them was a newly discovered species of coral, described by Couch in his subsequent report to the Royal Cornwall Polytechnic Society the following year as having 'branches as long and stout as a finger, and of a lively flesh colour, with the projecting polyps a pale white'. Gray named it *Rhodophyton couchii* in honour of its finder and in addition requested that Couch's growing collection of specimens in Polperro should be bequeathed to the British Museum.[13]

William Laughrin, the coastguard who had assisted with the dredging, was a much valued assistant to Couch in the doctor's pursuit of new species. It was Polperro's long history of involvement with the smuggling trade that had resulted in several coastguard officers being stationed there during the first half of the nineteenth century. Laughrin, whose duties involved patrolling the coast between Looe and Fowey, had ample opportunity to pursue his interest in natural history, keenly observing whatever he came across under Couch's direction and encouragement. So much so, in fact, that when he was promoted in September, 1857, to take charge of another coastguard station at Port Loe on the Roseland peninsula in West Cornwall, Couch went to extraordinary lengths to persuade the Customs Commissioners to keep him in Polperro, even involving John Edward Gray at the British Museum: 'I am deprived of a very useful assistant in my researches in

Natural History, for he preserved fishes exceedingly well, and dissected so as to form skeletons with the utmost skill and facility.'[14]

The campaign to keep Laughrin in Polperro succeeded and he was soon back there with his wife Amelia and their 11-year-old daughter Eliza Jane on Talland Hill, once more assisting Couch with his observations and discoveries. When Laughrin eventually retired from the coastguard service it was said that he became 'very skilful in anatomical manipulations, his preparations of fish, molluscs and crustaceans finding their way to many of our chief museums'.[15]

CHAPTER XVII

MAGNUM OPUS

Jonathan Couch's output of published work is remarkable both for its abundance and its diversity. Much of it was published during his lifetime. He wrote articles on the pilchard industry, the growth rate in crabs and lobsters, observations on diseases in lambs and poultry, an account of the skeleton of a porpoise washed ashore in Polperro; he wrote about whales observed off the Cornish coast, the midge fly that infects wheat, the habits of bats, the natural history of the salmon tribe, the migration of birds, marine fauna of Devon and Cornwall and much, much more.

One of Couch's earliest publications was *The Cornish Fauna*, the first part of which appeared in 1838, covering vertebrate animals and crustaceans. It attempted to classify and list brief details of every species of animal life then known to exist in Cornwall and, as a county record, was probably the first of its kind. Part two, covering testaceous molluscs, followed three years later while the third and final part, on zoophytes, was added by Couch's son Richard in 1844. The whole was intended as a companion to the museum collection of the Royal Institution of Cornwall at Truro, under whose auspices it was produced, adding as it did several new species to the list of British animals then known. It proved so popular that a second edition was published 40 years later in which Couch (posthumously) added a preface maintaining 'there is no county in England that presents such variation of aspect from all besides as does the county of Cornwall'.[1]

Many of his observations were included in his book, *Illustrations of Instinct deduced from the habits of British Animals*, published in August 1847 by John van Voorst, the London publisher of several works by William Yarrell and other British naturalists. Couch had spent nearly two years writing it, for which he received an advance of 40 guineas.[2] The 22 chapters cover such subjects as the nervous systems of animals, variations of habits, their disposition to become tame, the migration of birds and insects, and compassion shown to young birds by those of a different species. There is also a reference to Charles Darwin's account of his voyage aboard the *Beagle*, published eight years earlier.

Couch disagreed with English poets and philosophers who said the actions of man were governed by reason and animals by instinct. It was his considered opinion that animals and birds had an intellectual existence and the book was a first attempt to understand that in scientific terms. He devoted a chapter of his book to communication between man, birds and other animals by means of sounds which are not normal to either man or beast, ending it with the following self-evident truth written several decades before the conclusions of twentieth century animal psychologists such as Pavlov:

> 'A farmer's servant will assemble her company of pigs, and set them scampering with more than their wonted speed, at the rattle of a bucket and the accompaniment of a peculiar cry, which conveys no sound to which in a state of nature they could have been accustomed. And in the west of England, where oxen are universally employed in labour, a particular sound is employed to encourage them, which some boys are far better able to exert than others, and thus become more successful drivers; and of the variation of this, as it is drawled out, the cattle shew themselves duly aware, turning to the right or left, and proceeding more or less slowly, or stopping altogether, at the expression of tones altogether destitute of individual meaning.'[3]

He also tells the story of a small cupboard in his parents' house 'in which were kept milk, butter and other requisites for the tea-table; and the door was confined with a lock which, from age and frequent use, could easily be made to open. To save trouble the key was always kept in the lock, in which it revolved on a very slight impulse. It was often the subject of remark that the door of this cupboard was found wide open, and the milk or butter greatly diminished, without any imaginable reason, and notwithstanding the persuasion that the door had certainly been regularly locked; but it was accident that led to the detection of the offender. On watching carefully, the cat was seen to seat herself on the table; and, by repeated patting on the side of the bow of the key, it was at last made to turn, when a slight pull on the door caused it to move on its hinges'.[4]

Another example concerned a hedgehog that Couch once kept that was so timid the only way he was able to observe it move about was by viewing it through a crevice; at the least sound it would roll into a ball. It was eventually able to escape however by climbing a low wall by the harbour and throwing itself over, dropping a considerable distance to the sea below, 'but it swam in a right direction and landed in safety'.

The *Illustrations of Instinct* was well received. The *Examiner*, a popular radical weekly literary journal of the time, reviewed it favourably and said of the author:[5]

> 'His facts are of very great importance, and in his treatment
> and arrangement of them he has advanced very considerably
> the discussion of a highly important question. His anecdotes
> are as amusing, and sometimes as astonishing, as a fairy tale,
> and he makes them subserve his reasoning with great acuteness
> and skill.'

Darwin read it too and quoted several examples from it in a chapter on instinct he had originally written for his *Origin of Species* but which was published as a *Posthumous Essay on Instinct* shortly after his death in 1882. In one, referring to the nesting habits of the magpie, he writes: 'In Cornwall, Mr Couch says he has seen near each other, two nests, one in a hedge, not a yard from the ground "and unusually fenced with a thick structure of thorns"; the other "on the top of a very slender and solitary elm – the expectation clearly being

that no creature would venture to climb so fragile a column".[6] The
two men may not have communicated directly, but each had at least
read the other's published work.

As a schoolboy, Couch's Latin studies and classical education at the
hand of the émigré French priest at the Winsor Academy had led to
a life-long appreciation of the work of the great Roman naturalist
Pliny. Pliny the Elder (to distinguish him from his equally remarkable
nephew) was the author of an extraordinary encyclopaedia of natural
history completed in 37 volumes in 77AD, covering almost the entire
field of ancient knowledge including animals, birds, fish, insects
and plants. Pliny died a couple of years later while observing the
eruption of Vesuvius, but his *Naturalis Historia* remains one of the
largest single works to have survived from the Roman empire. The
only English translation of it at the beginning of the nineteenth
century was a rather long-winded version produced more than 200
years earlier, so Couch set about a more modern translation of his
own for the Wernerian Club, a short-lived London publishing society
that published academic works of particular interest to naturalists,
zoologists, botanists and collectors like himself.

It was an enormous undertaking that must have taken years of
painstaking work at his desk in Polperro in addition to the hours he
spent gathering material in Sir Harry Trelawny's library at Trelawne.
By 1847, he had completed his translation of the first ten volumes
of Pliny's Latin text and this was published as the first volume
of a Wernerian Edition, of which Couch had been appointed the
Superintending Editor. Of the original English version by Philemon
Holland he wrote, 'I found that translator exceedingly prolix, very
rarely mistaking the sense of his author, but adding to him by
way of comment, as if afraid that the reader would not otherwise
understand what was meant. Pliny, on the other hand, is concise,
even to occasional obscurity'.[7] One later reviewer of Couch's version
complained that it was 'bowdlerized, emasculated, modernized and
generally given the mid-Victorian treatment' but it would surely have
been a more popular read for anyone not wishing to wallow in some
of Holland's Elizabethan phraseology.[8]

What emerges from the pages of Couch's translation is an extraordinary affinity between two keen observers of the natural world across a span of 1,800 years. When Pliny writes about fish, for example, and says the Surmullet is among the best 'as well in Excellency and Flavour as in Plenty; but they are only of moderate Size, for it is uncommon them weigh above two Pounds', Couch adds a footnote to say that much heavier ones had been seen 'on the coast of Cornwall' as if he is addressing the great Roman author personally.[9] And when Pliny tells the story of Cleopatra dissolving her pearl earrings in vinegar before drinking it to impress Mark Antony, Couch suggests that she must have 'broke and pounded the pearls; and it is probable that she afterwards diluted the vinegar with water' before drinking it.[10] It is as if the two men were engaged in a dialogue across the centuries. Couch's son Thomas contributed some of the illustrations to the text of his translation and a second Wernerian volume followed before the club was disbanded. Although perhaps somewhat abstruse for modern readers, it was in every sense a *magnum opus* and stands alongside his other great but unpublished work, *Historical Biographies of Animals known to the Ancients*, much of which was translated from Hebrew manuscripts.

Jonathan Couch's true *magnum opus* remains his *History of the Fishes of the British Islands* published in four volumes between 1862 and 1865. If he had done nothing else in life except produce that work, he would still rank as a great naturalist. As it is the four volumes were a major publishing triumph, establishing his reputation as one of the world's leading ichthyologists. Yet he received a mere £50 for them, scarcely enough to cover the cost of his paper, pen, ink and postage.[11]

It was the culmination of some 60 years' observations and research, aided by numerous contributors. He began work on the first volume in the summer of 1860, just two years after his third marriage. It was initially published in monthly parts by Richard Groombridge & Sons at one shilling each and finally, in 1862, as Volume I for 17 shillings.

Each of Couch's own delicately water-coloured drawings of the fish, completed whilst the specimens were still alive, was engraved on boxwood by Alexander Francis Lydon, working with Benjamin Fawcett, one of Britain's finest nineteenth century woodblock colour printers. The engraved plates were then finished by hand, probably under the supervision of Fawcett's clever wife, Martha, at the firm's premises in Driffield, East Yorkshire. The fourth and final volume was eventually completed in 1865 and the complete set, with a total of 252 coloured illustrations, could be purchased from Groombridge & Sons in Paternoster Row, London for £3..16s.

In the preface to the fourth volume, Couch wrote that it had been his intention to make it easy for anyone to recognise each species, most of which had been drawn 'with their native colours fresh upon them'. He adds his belief that 'the inhabitants of water are not less furnished than those on land with the means of existence, and with faculties which enable them to turn what may appear to be unfavourable circumstances to good account'.[12] If his own plates that adorn the pages of the four volumes seem a little too brightly coloured, it must be remembered that in most cases he was able to receive the specimens fresh from the water before their lustre had become dulled.

Couch readily acknowledged the help he received over many years, including assistance from William Rashleigh, the former MP for Fowey who contributed a few of the illustrations. To establish and test his conclusions, he had corresponded with men all over Britain as far afield as the Shetland Islands and the Isles of Scilly. The Earl of Enniskillen sent him specimens of lake trout from Ireland and so did James Morrison MP, a rich Victorian merchant who fished Malham Tarn in Yorkshire.[13]

A review of the *History of the Fishes of the British Islands* in the *Zoological Record* in 1865 described it as 'a most complete account of the life and habits of British fishes, especially those observed by the author on the Cornish coast... a most useful and instructive book that may be easily read by every lover of natural history'.[14] The four solid volumes remain a standard work of reference even today, still consulted by anglers and other fishermen; though now scarce and eagerly sought by antiquarian booksellers, the coloured plates are more often offered for sale separately.

Couch's death in 1870 prevented his final published work, *The History of Polperro*, from appearing during his lifetime but his son Thomas ensured that it was published the following year. It contains a brief introductory chapter by Thomas on his father's life and says, by way of explanation for its belated appearance, 'though he had some vague notions of publication, a press of other engagements rendered this impossible'.[15] A chapter on smuggling and privateering recounts stories told to Couch of some of the more notorious exploits involving Polperro seafarers such as the Quillers and the 'smuggler's banker', Zephaniah Job.

The book includes detailed accounts of local mythology, witchcraft, festivals and folk-lore as well as a glossary of obsolete Cornish words, making it one of the best local histories ever published. Much of the material was gathered from his visits to his patients over many years, in the course of which he would listen to strange tales of ghosts and superstitions as he moved from one cottage to another, and he in turn would delight in passing them on.

A

HISTORY

OF THE

FISHES

OF THE

BRITISH ISLANDS.

BY JONATHAN COUCH, F.L.S.

VOL. IV.

CONTAINING SEVENTY-THREE COLOURED PLATES,
FROM DRAWINGS BY THE AUTHOR.

The works of the LORD are great, sought out of all them that have
pleasure therein.—PSALM cxi, v. 2.

LONDON:
GROOMBRIDGE AND SONS, 5, PATERNOSTER ROW.
M DCCC LXV.

CHAPTER XVIII

FAME AND ACCLAIM

The completion of the four volumes of the *History of the Fishes of the British Islands* in 1865 marked the pinnacle of Couch's achievement in his lifetime study of natural history. Now, at the age of 76, he had established himself as one of the foremost natural scientists of his generation whose opinion on a wide variety of scientific topics was eagerly sought and freely given. Honours were showered upon him thick and fast.

In 1866 he was elected a corresponding member of the Zoological Society at the special recommendation of his friend, Dr. John Edward Gray, Keeper of the zoological collection at the British Museum and President of the Society. In the same year he received a second bronze medal from the Royal Cornwall Polytechnic Society (having already been awarded two silver medals for earlier published work) for his report on a Mediterranean Filefish caught in a crab pot near Mevagissey.[1]

But with fame and acclaim came advancing years and with it occasional ill health. Early in 1867 Couch suffered a severe attack of bronchitis which brought him close to death. Confined to his bed for several weeks during March and April, he lapsed into intermittent bouts of delirium in the course of which he would preach long sermons, some of which were noted down by his friend and near neighbour, Edward Geake Hocken, sitting patiently by his bedside. On one occasion, while he recited the words of a hymn, his wife Sarah took up a hymn book and began turning the pages in an attempt to find it. Seeing this, he said, 'I don't think you'll find it there; it comes from here,' tapping his forehead with his finger and proceeding to sing it through to a well-known tune. This was all the more extraordinary since he had never been known to sing a tune before in his life, and when reminded of it later during his convalescence, he absolutely refused to believe it.[2]

While he was recovering from his illness, he was awarded a gold medal and diploma by the Committee of the Exposition Internationale des Pêches at Arcachon, near Bordeaux, for a paper on the *Natural History of Eels* and for his *History of the Fishes of the British Islands*. At the time, he was the only Englishman to have received the award.

Frank Buckland, the ebullient editor of the journal *Land and Water*, wrote of Couch's award: 'His numerous admirers must all agree that he is worthy of this distinction. It is very gratifying to see that the labourers in the practical branch of Ichthyology are held in such high esteem by our neighbours in France'.[3] This was praise indeed, coming from someone who had himself made natural history attractive to a mass readership and was regarded then much as David Attenborough is today. Like Couch, the big, bearded Buckland had trained as a surgeon before devoting himself to natural history and was appointed Inspector of Salmon Fisheries. The two men corresponded at length and Buckland, whose London home was famous for its menagerie and its varied menus of exotic animals, made several visits to Polperro to consult Couch on salmon.

Couch's daughter Bertha recollected one such visit:

> 'I well remember his hearty laugh when Mr. Couch took him into the long room on the Lansallos side of the house to show him some of his treasures; a room one-third dining room, two-thirds library – and the remainder curiosity shop! Two lines were found stretched across on which two small children were busily engaged hanging out their dolls' clothes for a make-believe dry. The museum was at the further end of the room, but the line was too high to be stepped over, and when Mr. Buckland, much to the delight of the little girls, refused to allow it to be taken down, the two savants must needs bow their heads, bend their backs and creep underneath'.[4]

Now in his 80th year, Couch was still busily employed sketching and recording some newly discovered tiny molluscs called foraminifera that had been brought up from the sea bed during a deep sea dredging operation. In one of his last letters to his son Thomas, he wrote 'it is not to be wondered at that so many of these objects are new when several of them have been living at a depth of at least three miles'.[5] This was even before the three year voyage of *HMS Challenger* whose scientific results famously laid the cornerstone of scientific oceanography and was perhaps one of Couch's final contributions to a lifetime study that laid such a splendid foundation for the future study of marine life of the Cornish seas.

Bronchitis continued to afflict him every winter. A particularly severe period of cold weather in February 1870 brought on yet another attack, made worse by his insistence on attending some of his more seriously ill patients. This latest spell of indifferent health did not, however, prevent him from sending yet another paper to the Zoological Society of London describing a new species of giant sea slug observed at Polperro.[6] But it was to be the last.

On the morning of Wednesday, April 13, 1870, Sarah brought him his breakfast in bed. She remained with him, sitting by his bedside while he dealt with some correspondence and read a newspaper before saying to his wife that he felt tired and would have a nap. And as he slept, Cornwall's great naturalist, philanthropist and physician died peacefully at his home in Polperro at the age of 81.

Sarah Couch had earlier sent a message to Stephen Clogg, the doctor and entomologist in East Looe, asking him to visit her husband in the hope that he could be persuaded to remain at home indoors for a few days. But by the time Clogg arrived at Polperro just before midday, Jonathan Couch was already dead, leaving Sarah and the three little girls, aged nine, seven and two, alone.[7]

The funeral took place on a warm Easter Monday, April 18, in the cemetery at Mabel Barrow near Lansallos where his second wife, Jane, was buried. A day of mourning was observed by all the inhabitants of Polperro, many of whom followed the funeral procession to the graveside.

Couch's grandson, Sir Arthur Quiller-Couch, attended the funeral at the age of six with his father, Thomas, and later gave a vivid description: 'A long line of fishermen with sashes across their blue jerseys, drawn up at attention while the coffin, to avoid the narrow stairs, was lowered from a window: after that the stuffiness of a funeral coach (I can smell it yet) as we crawled up an interminable hill, at a point of which, as the horses paused to draw breath, someone pointed out to me a fine chestnut tree planted by my grandfather over a well he had opened and dedicated; and so by zigzags up to a graveyard on the hill's very summit, flanked by the whitewashed chapel of Mabel Barrow'.[8]

> 'Bronzed and hardy fishermen, their faces bearing traces of tears of which they were not ashamed, and awed by the calamity which had befallen them; deputations from friendly societies, coastguards, representative men throughout the county, and a host of friends and acquaintances from the neighbouring towns, all showed the sorrow they felt. A sob from those within sight of the grave marked the lowering of the coffin; the stillness was again broken by someone in the crowd saying in a tearful voice, "Dear old man!" and all was over.'[9]

Tributes to the Polperro surgeon's life and contribution to natural science were many and fulsome. Typical was the obituary that appeared in the *Western Morning News*:

> 'As a scientific man, the forte of Mr Couch lay in careful observation and accurate description. Nothing could exceed his painstaking, his constant and watchful attention, and the unalloyed pleasure he found in every new discovery he made in science. Less than most men was he the slave of prejudice and preconceived notions. He was always willing to learn, and when a fresh specimen of a rare fish was brought to him, or one hitherto undescribed, he was exceedingly particular in every inquiry respecting its capture, and in gathering the smallest particle of information. These facts were carefully noted at the time if possible, and he thus lost no opportunity of adding to his own personal information, which was, in fact, adding to the intelligence and instruction of the world. His skill in dissecting the specimens brought under his notice was also of great value to science. It was the simplicity of his character

and the honesty of his convictions which gave such an air
of truth to all he wrote. He had no theories to build up, no
fixed opinions to uphold, and his highest pleasure was to be
a learner and a student. He was a patient worker; a builder up
of the facts of science rather than a great thinker or originator.
His papers were always welcomed by the learned, though they
might not invariably be exhaustive treatises on every subject he
took in hand. Alone in his native village, uninfluenced by the
crowds who cheer on men to great exertions, self-reliant, and
full of inward energy, he never flagged in his onward career till
death put an end to his loving toils.'[10]

Couch had made a final will less than three years earlier, leaving
the house and other property in Polperro to Sarah (unless 'she shall
have ceased to be my widow') and their three daughters Bertha, Sarah
and Clarinda. He also made special provision for the lifetime care of
his mentally disabled son Jonathan. The bulk of his library of medical
books and unpublished material was to be divided between his other
two sons, Thomas and John, and there were also instructions for a
'plain headstone with an inscription' to be placed at Mabel Barrow
where his second wife, Jane, was buried.[11] The granite obelisk that was
duly erected to the memory of them both still stands prominently in
the corner of the windswept burial plot by the little Ebenezer Chapel
at Lansallos:

ERECTED
TO PERPETUATE THE MEMORY OF
JONATHAN COUCH F.L.S.
SURGEON
WHO DEPARTED THIS LIFE
AT POLPERRO IN THIS PARISH
APRIL 13TH 1870
AGED 82 YEARS
ALSO OF **JANE QUILLER** HIS WIFE
WHO THERE DEPARTED THIS LIFE
SEPTEMBER 7TH 1857
AGED 68 YEARS

Jonathan and Jane lay together at last within a stone's throw of another grave; that of the Bronze Age chieftain whose barrow once dominated the skyline, now just a hump in a field and a name on the map.

Couch's concern for his son Jonathan's care was not misplaced. Now 50 years old, he had lived all his life in the care of his family in Polperro, a gentle giant of a man possessed with enormous strength but of a generally placid yet autistic nature. His nephew, Arthur Quiller-Couch, recalling a visit made by Jonathan to his father's grave at Mabel Barrow one day, described him as 'touched in the head or, as we put it in the west "not exactly".' Alone there, Jonathan was suddenly seized with indignation at what he regarded as neglect of the grave, pulled up some shrubs belonging to other graves and transplanted them around his parents' obelisk. The sacrilege was discovered, denounced and, in a short while, compassionately overlooked.[12]

Sarah honoured her husband's wishes and allowed Jonathan to remain with her while she remained an unmarried widow, and she was soon joined by her own widowed mother Eliza Roose. Little Clarinda, not even three years old at the time of her father's death, was baptised in March 1872 at the Polperro Methodist chapel. Sarah's eldest daughter, Bertha, in her account of her father's life published in 1891, tells of a petition being drawn up by a number of influential people requesting that Sarah Couch should be granted a pension in recognition of her late husband's public service. Many signatures were added by people throughout the country before it was eventually delivered to the Prime Minister, William Gladstone. 'Their disappointment was great when it was known that the Prime Minister did not see his way clear to grant a pension, but forwarded the sum of £50'.[13]

When Sarah and her daughters moved away from Polperro, the Couch family home became a public reading room and library, thanks to the efforts of Evelyn Rashleigh, a member of the influential Cornish family. Rashleigh was a great supporter of the fishing industry in Cornwall and wanted the room to be used by local fishermen so that Jonathan Couch's work could continue. The initial response from the Polperro fishermen was unenthusiastic however; 'some said they could not read, and others that as their fathers got by without education, so could they', he reported. But, within a few weeks of Jonathan Couch's Reading Room and Lending Library opening in

September 1876, it had attracted over 100 subscribers. 'The women, too, have thanked me; for the books are an occupation and an amusement when the men are away, and that their husbands, who formerly after a bad night's fishing would come home very cross, and often drunk, now are hardly ever drunk, and if ruffled at home, go to their club'.

Sarah remarried in the summer of 1880, this time to James Lean, the 68-year-old Registrar of births and deaths at Liskeard, only to be widowed again two years later. Bertha had already left home by this time to work as a governess and the simple-minded Jonathan was lodged with the Braddon family in Lansallos Street, a few doors from the family home in Polperro, until his death in 1897.

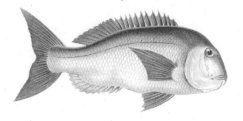

EPILOGUE

Jonathan Couch's son Thomas, entrusted with 'whatever manuscripts on scientific subjects may remain in my possession unpublished' at the time of his father's death, took on the daunting task of sorting through the considerable quantity of papers, notebooks, journals and unpublished work that had accumulated in the study of the house in Polperro where his father had worked for over 50 years.

Priority was given to *The History of Polperro* which was published the following year, despite the fact that most of the material for it had been gathered by Couch during his lifetime without much thought of publication. Thomas spent several months at his home at Bodmin editing and sorting the manuscript, largely gathered from written and oral accounts, adding a chapter outlining his father's life which he admitted was little more than a 'sketch'. He even went to the trouble of sending a draft to William Pengelly, the Cornish geologist who had collaborated with Jonathan Couch over the discovery of fossilised fish remains near Polperro in 1842. Inviting Pengelly's comments, Thomas explained that 'the claim of a harassing practice has not permitted me to keep *au courant* with the age in matters geological'.[1] Pengelly duly obliged and added his name to the list of 323 subscribers to the first edition.

Thomas died at Bodmin in 1884 at the age of 59, leaving three sons and two daughters. Arthur, the eldest, repeated his grandfather Jonathan's private assessment of Thomas as 'one of the best fellows that ever lived; you can trust him if all the rest of the world fails'.[2] When Jonathan had married Sarah, nearly 47 years younger than him, everyone in the family disapproved except Thomas, a fact that only served to strengthen the bond between father and son.

Under his celebrated nom-de-plume 'Q', Arthur Quiller-Couch paid his own tribute to his grandfather in a series of thinly-disguised vignettes celebrating his standing as a leader of the community, his methods of scientific study and the impression he left upon his own people of Polperro. One of his short stories, *Doctor Unonius,* features a fictional Cornish village named Polpeor:

> 'Polpeor, you must know, is a fishing-haven on the south coast of Cornwall, famous during the Napoleonic Wars for its privateering, and for its smuggling scarcely less notorious down to the middle of the last century. The doctor's parents, though of small estate, had earned by these and more legitimate arts enough money to set them dreaming of eminence for their only child, and sent him up to London to Guy's Hospital, where he studied surgery under the renowned Mr Astley Cooper. Having qualified himself in this and in medicine, he returned to his native home, which he never again left - save now and then for a holiday - until the day of his death.'[3]

Bertha Couch assumed the role of her father's biographer after the death of her step-brother, Thomas, and published the only detailed account of his life in a small monograph entitled *Life of Jonathan Couch F.L.S. etc. of Polperro: The Cornish Ichthyologist* in 1891. It is a charmingly affectionate portrait of her father complete with a frontispiece that includes a photograph of him sitting at his desk with a microscope, dressed in his familiar velvet collared frock-coat. In the preface, she says she had 'been persuaded that a short account of his life and labours would be acceptable to the many tourists' visiting Polperro, and acknowledged the help she received from her father's old friend and Wesleyan minister, Edward Geake Hocken, who had sat by his bedside writing down the sermons Couch delivered in a state of feverish delirium during one of his last bronchitic attacks.

Bertha's book was printed and published by John Philp of Liskeard who had been shrewd enough to spot the growing market for local history among the thousands of visitors who came to Polperro every year, attracted by the quaint charm of the cottages and harbour area.

Jonathan Couch's Reading Room and Lending Library had become Couch's Museum and Art Gallery by the 1920s where, according to *The Traveller and Clubman* magazine, 'original manuscripts and other relics of the great Jonathan Couch, the famous Cornish ichthyologist' could be viewed.[4] Over the years, signs proclaiming 'Couch's House – built 1595. Historic - Romantic' and 'The Lucky Cornish Pixie Shop' appeared as a tide of synthetic Cornish folklore engulfed the village.

Bertha's sister, Sarah, returned to Polperro in the summer of 1929 to unveil a white marble tablet in the Methodist church to the memory of her father.[5] Other members of the family were there, including Sir Arthur Quiller-Couch who told the gathering, 'even great men of science, recognising my name, have paid tribute to him as one who was a great observer and born naturalist, a man who never indulged in idle speculation, but always as an observer, never committing to paper anything of which he was not certain. And for that reason, after three generations, and in spite of all the discoveries of biology, men still delve into his work and still build upon it'.[6]

The inscription reads:

TO THE GLORY OF GOD
AND IN LOVING MEMORY OF
DR. JONATHAN COUCH F.L.S.
HE WAS ONE OF THE FIRST TRUSTEES OF THIS CHURCH.
THE DEEP PIETY WHICH MARKED HIS LABOURS AND
PREACHING HERE
PERMEATED ALSO HIS DEVOTED SERVICE TO HIS FELLOW
MEN, AND
TO LEARNING, AND WAS REFLECTED IN HIS MANY
WRITINGS ON
NATURAL HISTORY. HE WAS A LIFELONG SEEKER AFTER
TRUTH
BOTH IN THE WORLD AND IN THE WORKS OF GOD. HE
ENTERED INTO A
GREATER KNOWLEDGE AND A HIGHER SERVICE OF GOD ON
APRIL 13, 1870.
HIS MEMORY IS PRECIOUS AND ENDURES.

Today, the chapel itself has been replaced and the memorial tablet now lies in the garden of Couch's former home by the Saxon bridge in Polperro. The house itself is no longer open to visitors, having reverted to private ownership, but many of its original interior features are clearly discernible, including the parlour and study where Jonathan Couch penned so much of his correspondence, drafted manuscripts, made journal entries and sketched specimens for more than half a century. And on the other side of the harbour, a simple blue plaque on the outside of Warren Cottage commemorates his birthplace in 1789.

In a more recent tribute to his contribution to natural history, the Post Office issued a set of four postage stamps in January 1988 commemorating the bicentenary of the Linnean Society, one of which depicted the colourful short-spined sea-scorpion or bull-rout (*Mixocephalus scorpius*) reproduced from one of the illustrations in Couch's *History of the Fishes of the British Islands*. The Polperro surgeon and naturalist, writer of so many letters to fellow naturalists during his lifetime, would surely have been proud of such an honour.

Notes & References

I A Lively And Enquiring Mind

1. *The Private Memoirs of Jonathan Couch (1789-1870) of Polperro*, transcribed and edited by Alwyne Wheeler, Journal of the Royal Institution of Cornwall NS Vol. IX, Part II (1983).
2. Bertha Couch, *Life of Jonathan Couch* (1891): 12.
3. Couch, *History of Polperro (*1871): 4 *et. seq.*
4. *Sherborne Mercury* 2 April 1798.
5. Carole Vivian, *Cornwall Association of Local Historians Journal* (Spring 1998), 7.
6. Couch, *Private Memoirs* [RIC Journal 1983]. No priest called Arzell appears in Plasse, or in Catholic Record Society XII. A Mons. D'Ancel is mentioned in a letter dated 6 June 1798 as a suitable candidate to be president of a projected college: letter-book, Western Vicariate, 1798, item 74 (Bristol R.O. 35721 series); Dominic Aidan Bellenger, The French Exiled Clergy, Downside, 1986, lists no Arzell, but (p. 143) one named d'Ancel: Jean Charles Richard D'Ancel (1761-1836), of the diocese of Paris, a teacher [and probably identical with 'Fr. Arzell' who taught at Pelynt].
7. *Royal Cornwall Gazette*, 24 October 1801.
8. Bertha Couch, *Life of Jonathan Couch:* 16.
9. *Private Memoirs*, RIC Journal (1983*).*
10. Bertha Couch, *Life of Jonathan Couch:* 18.

II Looming Reality Of War

1. Bertha Couch, *Life of Jonathan Couch*: 19; Thomas Bond, *Topographical and historical sketches of the boroughs of East and West Looe* (1823):37.
2. Frank Kitchen, *Defence of the Southern Coast of Cornwall against the French Revolution*, Cornwall Association of Local Historians Journal (October 1990): 6.
3. *Ibid.*
4. *Private Memoirs.*
5. Harding, Mary, Diary (1812-1818), transcribed by Philip Correll 1993.
6. Bertha Couch, *Life of Jonathan Couch*: 23.

III Love At First Sight

1. Couch papers in the Courtney Library, RIC, Truro.
2. Couch *Memoranda*, inserted in his *Private Memoirs*, RIC.
3. R.C. Brock, *Life and Work of Astley Cooper* (1952): 110.
4. E.M. McInnes, *St. Thomas's Hospital* (1963).
5. D.C. Cameron, *Mr. Guy's Hospital 1746-1948* (1954): 149.
6. *Ibid.*
7. Bertha Couch, *Life of Jonathan Couch:* 25.

IV A Sudden And Brutal End

1. Couch *Memoranda,* inserted in his *Private Memoirs*, RIC.
2. Jonathan's occupation was given as Surgeon; Jane signed herself Jenny, probably a family soubriquet.
3. James Greig, ed., *The Farington Diary*, 8 vols., 1922-23, vol.6: 112 ff.
4. Todd Gray, *Cornwall: The Travellers' Tales* Vol. I (2000): 92.
5. Couch *Memoranda* [RIC].
6. *Private Memoirs.*
7. *Ibid.* (Loose sheet inserted).
8. Bertha Couch, *Life of Jonathan Couch:* 27.
9. *Ibid:* 28.

V Dreadful Times

1. *Private Memoirs.*
2. Bertha Couch, *Life of Jonathan Couch:* 33.
3. Diary of Mary Harding (1812-1818), edited by Philip Correll.
4. Couch, *History of Polperro:* 34.
5. ZJ52 (RIC).
6. *Private Memoirs.*
7. *Ibid.*
8. *Sherborne Mercury,* 29 November 1824.
9. Sheila de Burlet, *History of Polperro,* unpublished MS, RIC.
10. Bertha Couch, *Life of Jonathan Couch:* 55.
11. Couch, *Fishes of the British Islands*, Vol. IV: 416.
12. *Private Memoirs.*
13. R.D. Penhallurick, *Jonathan Couch's Cornish Birds* (2003): 119.

VI Rooks Of Trelawne

1. Mary Harding diaries (1812-1818).
2. *Ibid.*
3. Mrs Anna Eliza Bray, *Trelawny of Trelawne* (1837), 79.
4. Couch, *Journal of Natural History* (1805-1870) MS, Vol.I: .3 (RIC).
5. R.D. Penhallurick, *Jonathan Couch's Cornish Birds* (2003): 24.
6. Bertha Couch, *Life of Jonathan Couch:* 82.
7. Couch, *Journal of Natural History,* Vol. VII: 52.
8. *Ibid.* Vol. I: 96.
9. *Ibid.* Vol. VII: 52 et seq.
10. *Ibid.* Vol. VII: 35.
11. Couch, *Catalogue of Cornish Birds* (1829-1866), RIC.
12. R.D. Penhallurick, *Jonathan Couch's Cornish Birds:* 18.
13. *Journal of Natural History,* Vol. X: 399-402.
14. Correll, Philip, *Lewis Harding* (2000): 21.
15. Correll, Philip, *Lewis Harding, Photographer of Polperro*, privately published (1996).
16. Couch, *Illustrations of Instinct* (1847): 214.
17. *Private Memoirs.*
18. *Ibid.* Richard Opie may well have been related to the more famous John Opie.
19. Sheila de Burlet, *History of Polperro.*

VII Age Of Discovery

1. Bertha Couch, *Life of Jonathan Couch:* 29.
2. *Imperial Magazine,* August 1822.
3. Couch, *On a supposed unrecognized Fish of the genus Brama,* Penzance Natural History Society 1848.
4. Linnean Society of London Library.
5. A. T .Gage & W. T. Stearn, *Bicentenary History of the Linnean Society of London* (1988): 34 *et seq.*
6. SP247, Couch papers at the Linnean Society Library.
7. *Ibid.* SP253A.
8. *Ibid.* SP248. Wilson's Storm Petrel breeds on islands off the Antarctic but is not common well out to sea to the south and west of Britain.
9. *Private Memoirs.*
10. *Ibid.*
11. Couch, *Fishes of the British Islands* Vol. II: 81.
12. Couch MS, *British Fishes,* Linnean Society Library.
13. *Private Memoirs.*

VIII Wesley's Legacy

1. *Journal of John Wesley,* quoted in Couch's *History of Polperro:* 195.
2. *Ibid.*
3. *Ibid.*
4. Obituary of Zebedee Minards by Rev. William Davies, Wesleyan-Methodist Magazine, Vol. VII of 3rd series 1828: 857.
5. *Ibid.*
6. Todd Gray, *Cornwall: The Travellers' Tales* Vol. I (2000): 92.
7. Couch, *History of Polperro* (1871): 75.
8. The register for 1818-1837 is now at the National Archives, RG.4/846
9. *Wesleyan Magazine,* 1863: 569.
10. Paul Bolitho, *The Story of Methodism in the Liskeard Circuit 1751-1967:* 33-34.
11. *Records of the Wesleyan Association at Polperro:* MR.LISK/512, CRO. See also T.A.Shaw, *The Polperro Seceders: the record book of Dr. Jonathan Couch 1837-1869* in the Journal of the Cornish Methodist Historical Association, 1978.
12. *Ibid.*
13. Bertha Couch, *Life of Jonathan Couch:* 119.
14. Couch, *Illustrations of Instinct:* 161.

IX Refusal To Bury

1. *Private Memoirs.*
2. *Ibid.*
3. *Ibid.* No official record of Jane Rundle Hitchens' death exists; only an added footnote in the Lansallos burial register for 1847 giving her age incorrectly as 'about 16'. The next entry records the burial of Jane's grandmother, Margaret Hitchens, aged 77.
4. *Ibid.*
5. Couch, *History of Polperro:* 10.
6. *Private Memoirs.*
7. *Ibid.*
8. Carteret Priaulx papers, 22 April 1805. Priaulx Library, Guernsey.

X Cornish Ichthyologist

1. Couch, *History of Polperro:* 102.
2. Bertha Couch, *Life of Jonathan Couch:* 108.
3. Couch, *Natural History of the Pilchard* (1835).
4. Couch, *History of the Fishes of the British Islands* Vol. IV: 344.
5. *Ibid.* Vol. III: 77.
6. *Ibid.* Vol. II: 120.
7. *Transactions of the Penzance Natural History and Antiquarian Society* (1850): 396.
8. *Report of the Royal Cornwall Polytechnic Society* (1856): 27.
9. R.Q. Couch letter to his father, 9 July 1844 (RIC).
10. R.Q. Couch, *On the Metamorphosis of the Crustaceans,* 12th Annual Report of the Royal Cornwall Polytechnic Society, 1844.
11. Couch, *History of Polperro:* 103.
12. House of Commons: 2 June 1863 (Hansard Vol. 171 cc261-76).
13. Callum Roberts, *The Unnatural History of the Sea: The Past and Future of Humanity and Fishing* (2007).
14. Couch papers at the American Philosophical Society Library, Philadelphia.
15. F.E. Halliday, *A History of Cornwall* (1959): 291.
16. *Private Memoirs.*
17. *Plymouth, Devonport and Stonehouse Gazette,* May 1863.

XI Family Tradition

1. Sheila de Burlet *Jonathan Couch, Surgeon Apothecary of Polperro* (unpublished MS), RIC.
2. Couch papers at the RIC.
3. Thomas Quiller Couch letter, 9 October 1849, RIC.
4. *Ibid.*
5. Thomas Quiller Couch letter, 5 June 1852, RIC .
6. Jonathan Couch letter, 9 June 1852, RIC.
7. *Private Memoirs.*
8. Arthur Quiller-Couch, *Memories & Opinions* (1944): 5.
9. *Cornish Times*, 14 August 1858.
10. *Cornish Telegraph*, 31 July 1901.

XII A Deadly Disease

1. Couch, Medical Journal (1836-1841), RIC.
2. *Ibid.*
3. *Ibid.*
4. *Ibid.*
5. Bertha Couch, *Life of Jonathan Couch:* 103.
6. Couch, Medical Journal *op. cit.*
7. *Ibid.*
8. Couch papers at the American Philosophical Society Library, Philadelphia.
9. Couch, Medical Journal *op. cit.*
10. *Royal Cornwall Gazette*, 14 December 1849; *West Briton*, 1 February 1850.
11. Letter to Thomas Quiller Couch, 12 January 1850.
12. *West Briton*, 23 December 1853.
13. 1 January 1854: MH12/1431.
14. Bertha Couch, *Life of Jonathan Couch*: 55.
15. *Private Memoirs.*

XIII Man-Midwife

1. Couch, Medical Journal *op. cit.*
2. *Ibid.*
3. *Ibid.*
4. Harding, Mary, Diary (1812-1818), transcribed by Philip Correll 1993.
5. Couch, Medical Journal (1836-1841).
6. Loudon, Irvine., *Death in Childbirth* (1992): 185.
7. *Private Memoirs.*
8. Bertha Couch, *Life of Jonathan Couch*: 102.
9. Couch, *History of Polperro*: 149.

XIV A Good Horse

1. Loudon, I, *Medical Care and the General Practitioner 1750-1850* (1986): 117.
2. *Cornish Times*, 6 May 1932.
3. *Loudon's Magazine of Natural History* (1837).
4. Bertha Couch, *Life of Jonathan Couch*:156.
5. *Private Memoirs.*
6. Couch, *History of Polperro*: 41.
7. *Private Memoirs.*
8. *Cornish Times*, 24 September 1976.
9. *Private Memoirs*

10 Sir Charles Tennyson, *Alfred Tennyson* (1949): 327-328.
11. Letter to Richard Quiller Couch, 1846: RIC.
12. *Private Memoirs.*
13. Letter to Jane Couch, 12 August 1839: RIC.

XV 'Horrid Old Man'

1. *Private Memoirs.*
2. Couch papers at the RIC (1858).
3. Bertha Couch, *Life of Jonathan Couch*: 95 *et seq.*
4. *Private Memoirs.*
5. *Ibid.*
6. Bertha Couch, *Life of Jonathan Couch*: 120.
7. *Ibid.* 118.
8. Couch papers at the American Philosophical Society, Philadelphia.

XVI Mysterious Fossils

1. R.Q. Couch, *A Cornish Fauna Part III* (1844): vii.
2. *Private Memoirs.*
3. *Ibid.*
4. *Ibid.*
5. William Pengelly, *History of the Discovery of Fossil Fish in the Devonian Rocks of Devon and Cornwall* (1868).
6. *Ibid.*
7. *Private Memoirs.*
8. *Ibid.*
9. *Ibid.*
10. *Ibid.*
11. *35th Annual Report of the Royal Cornwall Polytechnic Society* (1867): 64 et. seq.
12. Bertha Couch, *Life of Jonathan Couch*: 58.
13. *Royal Cornwall Polytechnic Society Report* (1867): 69.
14. *Private Memoirs.*
15. Bertha Couch, *Life of Jonathan Couch*: 110.

XVII Magnum Opus

1. Couch, *A Cornish Fauna, Part 1* (2nd edition), RIC (1878):,.vi.
2. *Private Memoirs.*
3. Couch, *Illustrations of Instinct*: 123.
4. *Ibid.* 196.
5. *Examiner*, 16th October 1847.
6. Darwin, C. R., *Posthumous essay on instinct* (1883). London: Kegan Paul Trench & Co.: 355-384.
7. *Private Memoirs.*
8. R.D. Penhallurick, *Jonathan Couch's Cornish Birds:* 11.
9. Pliny *History of Nature*, Wernerian Club (1847). Vol.1, Book IX: 133.
10. *Ibid.* 156.
11. Bertha Couch, *Life of Jonathan Couch*: 115.
12. Couch, *History of the Fishes of the British Islands*, Vol IV: v-vi.
13. Sheila de Burlet, *Jonathan Couch, Surgeon Apothecary of Polperro*, RIC.
14. Denys Tucker, *A Cornish Ichthyologist in Fact and Fiction*, Journal of the Society for the Bibliography of Natural History (1956), Vol.3, Part 3: 137-151.
15. Couch, *History of Polperro:* 1.

XVIII Fame And Acclaim

1. Couch, *A filefish of the Mediterranean as distinguished from a species of the family (Balistes), that has been taken in Cornwall.* Annual Report of the Royal Cornwall Polytechnic Society (1866) no.34: 65-67.
2. Bertha Couch, *Life of Jonathan Couch*: 129.
3. *Ibid.* 117.
4. *Ibid.* 111.
5. Letter to Thomas Couch, 20 October 1869, RIC.
6. *Western Morning News,* 18 April 1870.
7. Bertha Couch, *Life of Jonathan Couch*: 130.
8. 'Q', *Memories & Opinions* (1944): 7.
9. *Ibid.* 131.
10. *Western Morning News* 18 April 1870.
11. Jonathan Couch's will, proved 8 June 1870; CRO. The inscription added gives Jonathan's age at the time of his death incorrectly (he was 81); also that of his wife Jane (she died aged 66).
12. 'Q', *Memories & Opinions*: 8.
13. Bertha Couch, *Life of Jonathan Couch*: 136.

Epilogue

1. Thomas Quiller Couch letter to William Pengelly, 27 June 1870, RIC.
2. 'Q', *Memories & Opinions*:: 8.
3. Arthur Quiller-Couch, *Corporal Sam & Other Stories* (1910).
4. *Traveller and Clubman*, September 1926.
5. Sarah Roose Couch had married a master mariner also named, confusingly, Jonathan Couch in 1884. Their son Jonathan was born in 1889.
6. *Cornish Times*, 16 August 1929.

Bibliography

Barton, R. M. *An Introduction to the Geology of Cornwall* (1964)

Brock, R.C. *The Life and Work of Astley Cooper* (1952)

Bray, Mrs A. E. *Trelawny of Trelawne* (1837)

Cameron, D.C. Mr Guy's Hospital 1746-1948 (1954)

Correll, Philip. *Lewis Harding, Photographer of Polperro* (privately published 1996)
   Lewis Harding – Cornwall's Pioneer Photographer (2000)
   Diaries of Mary Harding (1812-1818) (unpublished MS)

Couch, Bertha. *Life of Jonathan Couch* (1891)

Couch, Jonathan. *Illustrations of Instinct* (1847)
   A History of the Fishes of the British Islands (1862-1865)
   History of Polperro (1871)

de Burlet, Sheila. *Salt In The Cellars, Sand On The Fields* (unpublished MS)
   Jonathan Couch, Surgeon Apothecary of Polperro (unpublished MS)

Darwin, Charles. *Posthumous essay on instinct* (1883).

Derriman, James. *Killigarth: Three Centuries of a Cornish Manor* (1994)
   History of Talland (2007 unpublished MS)

Gage, A.T. & Stearn, W.T. *A Bicentenary History of the Linnean Society of London* (1988)

Grey, Todd. *Cornwall: The Travellers' Tales Vol. 1* (2000)

Halliday, F.E. *A History of Cornwall* (1959)

Hull, Brenda. *Thomas Q. Couch as a Medical Student* CALH Journal (April 1992)

Jenkin, A.K. Hamilton. *Cornwall and its People* (1945)

Johns, Jeremy Rowett. *The Smugglers' Banker* (1996)

Keast, John. *East & West Looe* (1987)

Kitchen, Frank. *Defence of the Southern Coast of Cornwall* etc. CALH Journal 1990

Knighton, Lady. *Memoirs of Sir William Knighton* (1838)

Lean, Garth. *John Wesley, Anglican* (1964)

Loudon, Irvine. *Medical Care and the General Practitioner 1750-1850* (1986)
   Death In Childbirth (1992) Clarendon Press

Murray, John. *A Handbook for Travellers in Devon and Cornwall* (1859)

Parsons, F.G. *History of St. Thomas's Hospital 1800-1900* (1936)

Pengelly, W. *The History of the Discovery of Fossil Fish in the Devonian Rocks of Devon and Cornwall,* Transactions of the Devonshire Association for the Advancement of Science (1868)

Penhallurick, R. D. *Jonathan Couch's Cornish Birds* (2003)
   Life In A Rookery (1847-1848) edited and transcribed (2001)

Perrycoste, Frank. *Gleanings from the Records of Zephaniah Job of Polperro* (1929)

Quiller-Couch, Arthur. *Corporal Sam & Other Stories* (1910)
   Memories & Opinions (1944)

Roberts, Callum. *The Unnatural History of the Sea: The Past and Future of Humanity and Fishing* (2007)

Tennyson, Charles. *Alfred Tennyson* (1949),

Trelawny, John. *The Trelawny Family* (1999)

Tucker, Denys. *A Cornish Ichthyologist in Fact and Fiction,* Journal of the Society for the Bibliography of Natural History (1956),

Wheeler, Alwyne. *Private Memoirs of Jonathan Couch,* Journal of the Royal Institution of Cornwall (1983)

Woodward, Llewellyn. *The Age of Reform: 1815-1870* (1962)

Appendix

Jonathan Couch's Family

Richard **COUCH** (1739-1823)
m. Philippa MINARDS 25/1/1788
(1744-1833)

<u>First marriage</u>

Jonathan COUCH (1789-1870)
m.1. Jane Prynn RUNDLE 14/8/1810
(1792-1810)

Jane Rundle COUCH (1810-1891)
m. Peter **HITCHENS** 9/7/1832
(1810-1846)

Richard   (1832-1867)

Jane Rundle (1834-1847)

Mary Elizabeth (1836-1853)

Hannah (1839-1914)

Sarah Ann (1841-1856)

Rebecca (1846-1897)

Second marriage

Jonathan COUCH (1789-1870)
*m.*2. Jane QUILLER 12/6/1815
(1790-1857)

Richard Quiller (1816-1863)
Surgeon
m. Lydia PEARCE 1853

Margaret Quiller (1817-1858)

John (1818-1826)

Jonathan (1820-1897)

Thomas Quiller (1826-1884)
Surgeon
m. Mary FORD 1863

John Quiller (1830-1900)
Surgeon

Arthur Thomas Quiller
(1863-1944)
(Q)

Third marriage

Jonathan COUCH (1789-1870)
m.3. Sarah Lander ROOSE 23/10/1858
(1836-1923)

|

Bertha
(1860-1942)

Sarah Roose
(1862-1945)
m. Jonathan COUCH (1884)

Lydia
(1863-1863)

Clarinda
(1867-1944)
m. Henry SHERWOOD 1897